Reviews

Tell Us a Sick One Jakey
'This book is quite repulsive!' Sir Michael Havers, Attorney General

Never Alone with Rex Malone
'A ribald, ambitious black comedy, a story powerfully told.'
Stewart Steven, *The Daily Mail*

'I was absolutely flabbergasted when I read it!' *Robert Maxwell*

Robert Maxwell as I Knew Him
'One of the most amusing books I have read for a long time. Eleanor
Berry is an original.' Elisa Segrave, *The Literary Review*

'Undoubtedly the most amusing book I have read all year.' Julia
Llewellyn-Smith, *The Times*

'With respect and I repeat, with very great respect, because I know
you're a lady, but all you ever do is just go on and on and on and on
about this bleeding bloke!' *Reggie Kray.*

Cap'n Bob and Me
'A comic masterpiece.' *The Times*

'As befits the maternal granddaughter of F.E. Smith (famous barrister
who never lost a case) Eleanor Berry has a sharp tone of phrase
and a latent desire for upsetting people. Campaigning for her hero,
Robert Maxwell, in a General Election, she climbed to the top of the
Buckingham Town Hall and erected the red flag. Eleanor Berry fits into
the long tradition of British eccentricity.' Stewart Graham, *The Spectator*

Someone's Been Done Up Harley
'Eleanor Berry's dazzling wit hits the Harley Street scene. Her
extraordinary humour had me in stitches.'
Thelma Masters, *The Oxford Times*
O, Hitman, My Hitman!

'Eleanor Berry's volatile pen is at it again. This time, she takes her readers back to the humorously eccentric Harley Street community. She also introduces Romany gypsies and travelling circuses, a trait which she has inherited from her self-confessed gypsy aunt, the late writer, Eleanor Smith, after whom she was named. Like Smith, Berry is an inimitable and delightfully natural writer.' Kev Zein, *The Johannesburg Evening Sketch*

McArandy was Hanged on the Gibbet High
'We have here a potboiling, swashbuckling blockbuster, which is rich in adventure, intrigue, history, amorous episodes and above all black humour. The story Eleanor Berry tells is multi-coloured, multi-faceted and nothing short of fantastic.' Angel Z. Hogan, *The Daily Melbourne Times*

The Adventures of Eddy Vernon
'Rather a hot book for bedtime.' the late Nigel Dempster, *The Daily Mail*

Stop the Car, Mr Becket! (formerly The Rendon Boy to the Grave is Gone)
'This book makes for fascinating reading, as strange, black-humoured and entertaining as Eleanor Berry's other books which came out before it.' It is to be noted that Eleanor is embarrassed by parts of this book. *Gaynor Evans, Bristol Evening Post*

Sixty Funny Stories
'This book is a laugh a line.' Elisa Segrave, writer and diarist

The House of the Weird Doctors
'This delightful medical caper puts even A.J. Cronin in the shade.' Noel I. Leskin, *The Stethoscope*

The Most Singular Adventures of Sarah Lloyd
'A riotous read from start to finish.' Ned McMurphy, *The Irish Times*

Alandra Varinia – Sarah's Daughter
'Eleanor Berry manages to maintain her raw and haunting wit as much as ever.' Dwight C. Farr, *The Texas Chronicle*

The Rise and Fall of Mad Silver Jaxton
'This time, Eleanor Berry tries her versatile hand at politics. Her sparkling wit and the reader's desire to turn the page are still in evidence. Eleanor Berry is unique.' Don F. Saunderson, *The South London Review*

About the Author

Eleanor Agnes Berry is the author of 24 published books and says her first brush with literature was when she broke windows in Ian Fleming's house at the age of eight. 'He struck me as being a singularly disagreeable man, with no understanding of children,' she recalls. Of Welsh ancestry, she was born and bred in London. She holds a BA Hons degree (a 2:2) in English.

Eleanor specializes in black humour. In many of her books, there is a firm of funeral directors called Crumblebottom and Bongwit. The works of Gorki, Dostoevsky, Gogol, Edgar Allan Poe, James Hadley Chase, George Orwell, Joe Orton and William Harrison-Ainsworth have strongly influenced her writings. While at university she completed an unpublished contextual thesis on the Marquis de Sade (whom she refers to as 'de Soggins'). In her spare time she wrote a grossly indecent book, entitled, *The Story of Paddy*, which she had the good sense to burn, and inadvertently set a garage on fire.

After leaving university she worked as a commercial translator, using French and Russian. She then worked as a debt collector for a Harley Street specialist, namely the late Dr Victor Ratner, and has since worked intermittently as a medical secretary. She was unfairly sacked from St Bartholomew's Hospital in London because she had been a close friend of the late Robert Maxwell's. (She had worked there for five years!)

Two of her novels are available in Russian and a third, which she refrains from naming, is currently being made into a film.

Eleanor is the author of numerous articles in *The Oldie* magazine and has appeared on television and on radio several times, including Radio California. Her interests include Russian literature, Russian folk songs, Irish rebel songs, the cinema, amateur piano playing, sensational court cases, the medical profession, entertaining her nephews, to whom she is extremely close, and swimming across Marseille harbour for kicks. When she dies, she will have her ashes scattered over Marseille harbour, her favourite place.

Eleanor Berry is the maternal niece of the late, famous, self-confessed gypsy author, Eleanor Smith, after whom she was named. Sadly, Eleanor Smith died before Eleanor Berry was born.

Books by Eleanor Berry

The Story of Paddy (A pornographic book – not published)
Tell Us a Sick One Jakey (Out of print)
Never Alone with Rex Malone (A black comedy about Robert Maxwell's alleged relationship with a crooked funeral director – Out of print)
Someone's Been Done Up Harley
O, Hitman, My Hitman!
The Adventures of Eddy Vernon
Stop the Car, Mr Becket! (Formerly *The Rendon Boy to the Grave Is Gone*)
Robert Maxwell as I Knew Him (Out of print)
Cap'n Bob and Me (Out of print)
McArandy was Hanged on the Gibbet High
The House of the Weird Doctors
Sixty Funny Stories
The Most Singular Adventures of Sarah Lloyd
Alandra Varinia – Sarah's Daughter
The Rise and Fall of Mad Silver Jaxton
By the Fat of Unborn Leopards
The Killing of Lucinda Maloney
My Old Pal was a Junkie (Available in Russian)
Your Father Had to Swing, You Little Bastard! (Also available in Russian)
An Eye for a Tooth and a Limb for an Eye (A Story of Revenge)
Help me, Help me, It's Red!
Come Sweet Sexton, Tend My Grave
My Face Shall Appear on the Banknotes
My Unique Relationship with Robert Maxwell – The Truth At Last

'This is a dark, disturbing but at the same time hilarious tale of a megalomaniac dictator by the always readable and naughty Eleanor Berry.' The late Sally Farmiloe, award-winning actress and author

By the Fat of Unborn Leopards
'Could this ribald, grisly-humoured story about a right-wing British newspaper magnate's daughter, possibly be autobiographical, by any chance?' Peggy-Lou Kadinsky, *The Washington Globe*

'Fantastically black. A scream from beginning to end.'
Charles Kidd, Editor of *Debrett's Peerage*

The Killing of Lucinda Maloney
'This is the funniest book I've read for months,' Samantha Morris, *The Exeter Daily News*

My Old Pal was a Junkie
'Eleanor Berry is to literature what Hieronymus Bosch is to art. As with all Miss Berry's books, the reader has a burning urge to turn the page.'
Sonia Drew, *The Texas Times*

Your Father Had to Swing, You Little Bastard!
'A unique display of black humour which somehow fails to depress the reader.' Craig McLittle, *The Rugby Gazette*

'This book is an unheard of example of English black humour. Eleanor Berry is almost a reincarnation of our own beloved Dostoevsky.' Sergei Robkov, Russian magazine, *Minuta*

An Eye for a Tooth and a Limb for an Eye: A Story of Revenge
'Words are Eleanor Berry's toys and her use of them is boundless.'
Mary Hickman, professional historian and writer

Help Me, Help Me, It's Red!
'Despite the sometimes weighty portent of this book, a sense of subtle, dry and black humour reigns throughout its pages. The unexpected twist is stupendous.'
Stephen Carson, *The Carolina Sun*
'This is grim humour at its very best. The most challenging and most delightful novel I have read in six months.' Scott Mason-Jones, *The New York Globe*

Come, Sweet Sexton, Tend My Grave
'Breathtakingly black, a treasure to read from beginning to end.'
Grace Ponsonby, *Newsweek*

My Face Shall Appear on the Banknotes
'Tightly paced and bitter-sweet throughout throughout.'
Alexis Lawrence, *The Cork Evening News*

'A satisfying and fantastic read in all ways.'
George Cullen

My Unique Relationship with Robert Maxwell – the Truth at Last
'A scholarly, moving but at the same time, delightfully comic work, seeped in black humour – a genuine page-turner.

This is the most entertaining book, I have read so far about the controversial Mirror Magnate and Eleanor Berry's friendship with him.

So far we have only heard negative things about him, but Eleanor has shown his human, kind and compassionate side, hitherto unknown to the British public.

John Cohen, *The Oxford Times*

MY UNIQUE RELATIONSHIP WITH ROBERT MAXWELL

THE TRUTH AT LAST

Eleanor Berry

www.eleanorberry.net

Also available on You-Tube and

Amazon

The Book Guild Ltd

First published in Great Britain in 2019 by
The Book Guild Ltd
9 Priory Business Park
Wistow Road, Kibworth
Leicestershire, LE8 0RX
Freephone: 0800 999 2982
www.bookguild.co.uk
Email: info@bookguild.co.uk
Twitter: @bookguild

Typeset in Baskerville

Printed and bound in Great Britain by CPI Group (UK) Ltd, Croydon, CR0 4YY

ISBN 978 1912362 899

British Library Cataloguing in Publication Data.

A catalogue record for this book is available from the British Library

For Ian Maxwell

Introduction

I have written three books about Robert Maxwell. I am sorry that this has been necessary. However, unlike the first two books, the third book is devoid of raunchiness, vulgarity and other literary flaws. The first two books greatly upset his widow.

The first book I wrote about him was entitled, *Robert Maxwell as I Knew Him*. This book has been sold out, but it was not only appallingly written; it was written in a hurry.

The reviewers were unanimous in saying that, though the book was extremely amusing, my literary style was "dreadful". In fact, my prose was packed with clichés and contained the occasional unending, verbose paragraph. Much of the writing in this book was puerile and unreadable.

The fact that *Robert Maxwell as I Knew Him*, was flawed, prompted me to write a second book about him, which was entitled, *Cap'n Bob and Me*.

My brother, Nicky (alas dead) egged me on a bit and dared me to write the second book in a really racy manner. I confess that I was slightly inebriated, whenever I sat down to write it.

Regrettably, *Cap'n Bob and Me* is saturated with sexual innuendo and even necrophile fantasies about the main protagonist.

I got carried away and implied, in places, that my relationship with the tortured *arriviste* had been sexual. I deeply regret having done this, and having misled, not only my readers, but also members of the Maxwell family.

The grammar in *Cap'n Bob and Me* is faulty in a number of places, but, fortunately, the book is not overtly drenched in clichés, as is *Robert Maxwell as I Knew Him*.

Cap'n Bob and Me has also been sold out, although it had favourable reviews in *The Spectator* and *The Times*.

I am deeply saddened and ashamed of the perverse, sexual and necrophile fantasies which appeared in *Cap'n Bob and Me*. Nicky cheered me up by saying I was a "literary bandit".

Several months passed, following the publication of this book. One morning, quite unexpectedly, I received a somewhat punitive letter from Bob's wretched widow, Betty.

In her letter, she rightly stated that her husband had been a father figure in my life, and a father figure only.

Although I was fiercely attracted to him, no sexual relations took place between us, at any time or in any place.

I was, and still am, filled with regret for having upset Betty, who had always been a surrogate mother to me.

In her letter, she stated that she had known, from the first day I met her, about my "infatuation" for her husband. Hers were strong words indeed, and were my sole motive for writing the third book about him, entitled *My Unique Relationship with Robert Maxwell – the truth at last*.

I did everything in my power to make amends. I took a bouquet of flowers to her flat in London. I sat on an upright, wooden chair, opposite her, with my head lowered in embarrassment.

"I'm terribly, terribly sorry but my pen got out of control," I ventured.

"It did! It did! You're so right," Betty replied mildly.

On the comic side, Nicky was amused by our exchange of words. He was dying but refused to let me know he was dying.

There was a long silence during my conversation with Betty.

"I hope, with all my heart, that one day you will think about forgiving me," I said eventually, but she didn't reply.

I left her flat. Very sadly, our relationship was never quite the same after that. Also, I was in hospital at the time of her funeral and could not attend it.

I don't know whether the dead can see the living, but I have a gut feeling that Betty has witnessed the writing of my third and final book about her husband.

As for Bob, I am sure he has forgiven my vanity and treachery.

My third book is comical in places and contains a number of humorous anecdotes, at the end of the book, which I have presented as a black comedy. I specialize in black humour and have always done so.

My prose in the third book is devoid of clichés, pornographic innuendo and necrophile fantasies.

* * *

On 31 May 2018, I visited Bob's grave on the Mount of Olives in Jerusalem and it was an honour to do so.

I laid three large stones on the grave, to indicate that I had visited it, and with the help of the Sexton, I lit two candles.

I knew that Bob could see me doing this, and that, if he had disapproved of any material in the first two books I had written about him, he was certainly touched by the contents of the third book, and by my visit to his grave. When I was there, I felt an uplifting, celestial and wonderful presence, as if he were actually alive and looking at me.

I spoke to him at length and thanked him for having saved my life, as the readers of this book will find out about, and also for showing me round the *Mirror*, on the last occasion I met him. I also told him how proud I was to have been his friend, whatever his faults may have been.

Unfortunately, I got sunstroke which was just as well, as the Sexton wanted to go home to have his lunch.

I am relieved by the fact that I have finally visited Bob's grave, and I am enormously grateful to my friends, Charlotte Spry and Dartagnon, whose surname I do not know.

Both accompanied me to Jerusalem and made my divine mission possible.

Eleanor Berry

LONDON

During the late nineteen-sixties, a hulk of a man, who looked like a beautiful, big black bear, was easing his Rolls down the Mall towards Buckingham Palace.

He approached the roundabout, where a statue of Queen Victoria, her face solemn and her hand holding the royal orb, peered formidably down upon him.

His car phone rang.

"Yes?" he barked.

"So then, Mr Maxwell, what are you doing about your overdraft?"

The caller's voice lacked the gutless, simpering whine which invariably infuriated Robert Maxwell. It was loud, distinct and strident, as if its owner were uninhibited and incapable of fear.

"Who the hell are you?" asked Maxwell, who was mildly irritated, but at the same time impressed by the caller's boldness.

"My name is Nicholas Berry. I'm the financial correspondent of *The Daily Telegraph*."

"Would you like to come to my house for a drink this evening, Mr Berry? I live in Fitzroy Square I like your style."

The house in which Bob met Nicky, for the first time, was dark but tastefully decorated. They went into the living room and talked for a while. It became clear that they got on.

"My birthday's coming up," said Bob, towards the end of the conversation. "It's on 10th June. Have you got any brothers or sisters?"

"Yes, a brother and two sisters," said Nicky, who had become bored with hearing about Bob's overdraft.

Bob shoved a thick cigar into his mouth, undid the top two buttons of his shirt and loosened his tie. He often did this. It never failed to excite and enthral me. He took a sip of the champagne which he and Nicky had been drinking, and put his feet on an occasional table.

"Do your siblings live in England?" he asked.

"My elder brother is covering a story in America. One of my sisters is abroad. My youngest sister lives in London."

Bob took another sip of champagne and lit his cigar which had gone out.

"Your sister, who lives in London, what's her name?" he asked.

"Eleanor."

"How old is she?"

"In her mid-to-late teens."

"Why don't you bring her to my birthday party on Saturday, Nicholas? I live at Headington Hill Hall in Oxford."

"Thank you, Bob. I'll bring her along," said Nicky, adding, "Is it all right if I bring my girlfriend as well?"

"Of course. I'd like to meet her."

My family were staying in our house in Buckinghamshire. Nicky drove his girlfriend and me to Oxford and from there to Headington Hill Hall. Before we set out, Nicky turned to me and said, half seriously and half in jest, "Just thought I'd tell you, old bean, Robert Maxwell's original family were Holocaust victims, so will you be sure to put your most gracious foot forward, and refrain from talking to him about dead bodies in mortuaries!"

Nicky's girlfriend was weird. Her name was Anne de Chauvigny and she blew hot and cold air. She was French and was typical of her fellow-countrymen. Sometimes, she was charming; other times, she was stone cold. Nicky was hopelessly in love with her and wanted to marry her, but she married a man called David Medcalfe instead. (Medcalfe was richer than Nicky. That says it all.)

Nicky fought to the death to persuade Anne to marry him, even though she had become engaged to Medcalfe. Often, once they had married, Nicky invited her out to lunch and insisted that I accompany him. Perhaps he wanted moral support.

I had always been close to Nicky. My affection for him was due to the fact that he never tried to get into my head. Also, he saw a funny side to all things grave and never showed emotion. I do not like showing any emotion, except anger. I can give an example of Nicky's distaste for emotion. Commenting on the brilliantly written but tragic novel, *Lady Chatterley's Lover*, he remarked that the book was "damned amusing." He added, "things get a bit dicey at the end, though." It was his stiff upper lip personality which endeared him to Bob.

Throughout the journey to Oxford, I talked incessantly and Anne laughed at my jokes. Once we had arrived at Bob's house, however, she suddenly became earth-shatteringly cold, as if she had taken something.

Nicky was absolutely besotted by this woman and turned up at her wedding ceremony to Medcalfe. He scowled at the groom throughout the service. Finally, Nicky split up with Anne.

"It was the best thing I ever did in my life!" he told me at a later date.

Anne was moderately pretty. She had short, fair, curly hair and a straight nose.

Nicky introduced me to Bob, who was standing in a marquee on the lawn of his house, wearing a white bath-towel dressing-gown and chewing an unlit cigar.

I danced with him. It suddenly dawned on me that he generated a livid, brutal and astonishing sexuality. There was something God-like about him. The first thing I asked him for was his permission to address him as "Bob".

"Of course, you can call me Bob," he said, "When in doubt, be brash like myself."

"How many children have you got, Bob? My mother said you had a big family."

"Seven. I'm afraid I used to have nine. My youngest daughter, Karine, died of leukaemia in 1957, and my eldest son, Michael, died following a road accident. He was in a coma for a long time before we turned his life support machine off."

"I'm so very sorry," I said.

Bob waved his hand in the air dismissively, as if he were driving away a fly. He continued, "Philip is my eldest son now. Then there's Anne. After that, come my twins, 'Isabel and Christine.'"

I noticed some pride in his voice when he referred to "my twins". He had spoken in a tone of almost childlike endearment, which made me feel another surge of attraction towards this man with his guttural Cossack's laugh and velvet, booming voice.

At that time, I had no idea that his twins had hovered between life and death in infancy. Bob had driven like one possessed, sometimes mounting the pavements of the cobbled streets of Paris. He looked frantically for the nearest hospital, where the twins were saved, just in time.

"What about your other children?" I asked.

"I have a son called Ian. Next in age, comes Kevin and then there's Ghislaine. She's my youngest. She's a little terror!"

The band lashed out with some heavy jazz.

Bob led me to the centre of the dance floor. He twirled me round and round until I was giddy.

"Go into the swimming hut, next to the pool, and put on a bathing suit," he said suddenly. The bathing suit I put on was extremely tight. It would have made the bathing suit worn by Christine Keeler at Clivedon, look like an outsized maternity dress in comparison.

Bob asked me if I could swim. Then he picked me up and threw me into the pool. I swam round in circles and finally got out of the water. Bob's wife, Betty, put a hot sausage into my mouth as I was climbing up the ladder.

"This is straight from the barbecue, Eléanore. Eat it before it gets cold." She had a strong French accent. Bob had just introduced us.

"What a lion of a man and what a resplendent rose of a woman, thought I. A lot of women fancied her husband madly, but she knew neither vindictiveness nor envy. All she wanted to do was to make others happy. She was not typical of French women.

I saw Bob dancing with Anne de Chauvigny. She was flirting outrageously with him, probably because she had a *penchant* for millionaires. Nicky and I were absolutely furious.

I had had quite a lot to drink by the time Nicky took Anne and me home. I talked a lot about Bob and said how attractive I thought he was.

"I knew all along you would get on with the Bouncing Czech," said Nicky.

"Why do you call him the 'Bouncing Czech'?" I asked.

"Because, as a businessman, he's considered by some to be hot enough to fry an egg on."

Bob hailed from a village called Solotvyno in the Carpathian Mountains, which had formally belonged to Czechoslovakia.

He was Jewish. Nearly all the members of his family were murdered by the Nazis, including his beloved mother. Only his sisters, Brana and Sylvia survived the concentration camps.

His original name was Jan Ludwig Hoch. He and his family preferred the Jewish version of his name, which was Abrahim Leib Hoch. He was the youngest child. He adored his mother whose name was Hannah.

His first ambition, when he was about thirteen, was to own a cow and a field.

He was relieved, beyond belief, when he heard that his two sisters had survived the Holocaust. I once took his sister, Sylvia Rosen, a fairly robust-looking lady, to see the film, *A Clockwork*

Orange. Unfortunately, Sylvia disliked the film. Bob was not too pleased, because he had wanted us both to canvass for him that afternoon.

Bob's mother was the greatest love of his early life. She had dark hair, a gentle, saintly face and eyes which gave out nothing but love. She had a look of serenity about her face. In a way, it resembled that of the *Mona Lisa*.

Bob had one very guilty secret. This had nothing to do with his career, or his financial dealings or his new family. As a soldier, he was heroic and his fellow soldiers admired his fearlessness.

However, he had one fear. He was absolutely terrified of his father. Apart from the Nazis' activities, his memories of his foul-tempered, bullying father plagued him throughout his later life, probably because he was ashamed of being afraid of anything or anyone.

His father was called "Mehel" (Michael) and he looked quite frightening in the one photograph I have seen of him. He had a pointed beard, like that of a wizard and mad-looking, piercing black eyes.

On one occasion, his youngest son was sick in the village street. Mehel grabbed him by his hair and rubbed his face in the vomit.

The beatings, which the boy received from his father, these were violent and often broke his skin, even if he was wearing rags.

Although Bob beat his own children, I am sure he refrained from doing so, in the savage way in which his father had beaten him. One of his children, whom I will not name, told me that he used to receive six-strokes, fully clothed.

It is known throughout the world, how heroically and courageously, Bob had fought the Germans during World War II, and how he had left Czechoslovakia on foot. His trek across Europe was legendary, and for the sake of brevity, I will not give details of his exceptionally brave exploits on his way to England.

Eventually he came into contact with Field Marshall Montgomery.

"I have no relatives and I've got nothing to lose," he shouted when in front of the Enemy's guns, "Shoot me dead if you wish, as long as you give me the Military Cross."

Struck by the young man's bravery, Montgomery pinned the medal to his chest. He was not shot. He lived until the age of sixty-eight.

* * *

It was in the late nineteen sixties that there had been some ominous talk about another airport, being built in Buckinghamshire. Bob was the Labour MP for North Bucks, and pressure was being put on him to be more vehement in his speeches about the horrors that the building of another airport posed.

Trees, scattered all over Buckinghamshire, were covered with drawings of livid-looking farmers, brandishing pitchforks. Captions underneath the drawings said, "Airport? Not over our dead bodies!"

* * *

Nicky told my father that I had got on well with Bob. Naturally, my father was very concerned about the threat of a new airport. Had it been built, nearly all the residents of Buckinghamshire would have had to leave their homes.

I was close to my father, who was good-natured, hard-working and stubborn. Once he got an idea into his head, he stuck to it like a terrier with a rubber ball in its mouth. I attribute this to the fact that he was a Welshman.

He and I were sitting in the dining room after lunch.

"I know all about you and Bob Maxwell," he said, in a slightly confrontational tone of voice.

"You talk as if something improper had taken place between us. Why did you say that?"

"I didn't mean it that way. I know you're a great friend of his. I have nothing against your friendship."

"Is there a problem?" I asked.

"Yes, there is. I'm referring to the proposed airport which would make the whole of Buckinghamshire uninhabitable."

I poured myself more ginger beer and drank some of it.

"I understand that. I don't really see what I can do about it."

"I'll tell you," my father began, "To fight the building of this airport, we need funds. So far, we haven't received anything from Uncle Bob." (He often referred to Maxwell as Uncle Bob.)

I drank some more ginger beer.

"I don't mind going over to Headington Hill Hall and asking Bob for money. I know he'll give me a cheque if I ask him nicely," I said.

My father looked at me out of the corner of his eye, half suspiciously, half amused.

"Oh, so you're as close as that, are you?" he asked.

"I told you there is nothing improper going on between us. I'll ring Bob up this afternoon and I'll invite myself to tea. Then, I'll ask him to write out a cheque. Who is the cheque to be made out to, and how much do you want me to ask him for?"

"We need at least five thousand pounds," said my father, in a deadpan tone of voice.

"That's a lot but I'll do my best."

"That really is very sporting of you."

After lunch, I dialled Bob's number. Betty answered.

"Sorry to bother you, Betty. Could I please speak to Bob?"

"Yes. He's in the garden. I'll call him for you."

(I noted that she showed no awkwardness or reluctance towards my speaking to her husband.)

Bob came onto the line.

"Yes, Eleanor?"

I had never forgotten his words, "When in doubt, be brash like myself."

"May I please come to tea with you, at about five o'clock this afternoon?" I asked.

"Yes, of course, you can. We look forward to seeing you."

I had not yet passed my driving test, so I had to be chauffeur-driven everywhere, if I was not travelling by bus or train.

My parents' driver was called "Mr Brightwell". Before I tell you about his memorable encounter with Robert Maxwell, I'd better tell you a bit about Mr Brightwell first. He is dead now. He looked like an old gnome. He was hot-tempered and fearfully forthright, although fundamentally he had a very kind heart.

He had such a murderous temper when provoked, that he would have made Ivan the Terrible seem like the owner of a home for birds with broken wings in comparison.

When I was a child, I enjoyed provoking Mr Brightwell, because I loved to see him in a rage. I once poured gravel into his bowl of clean oil, which he was about to pour into the engine of my father's car.

Mr Brightwell's rage was indescribable.

Apart from being hot-tempered, he was a bit of a ladies' man. His wife, May, had been my mother's maid. One morning, she came into my mother's bedroom in tears, because of her husband's infidelity towards her.

"Pull yourself together, dear. He'll soon come to heel," said my mother.

On this occasion, many years later, I got into my father's navy blue, hearse-like Ford Estate, and asked Mr Brightwell to take me to Headington Hill Hall. I gave him directions. The journey took us just over half an hour.

"I understand you was only expected for tea," said Mr Brightwell, rather aggressively, adding "I 'ope you're not going to dawdle. I missed *Dad's Army* last week, and I'll be blowed if I'm going to miss it again!"

I got out of the car and walked towards a group of men, who had gathered in the drive, just outside the Maxwells' house.

I recognized Bob, who was casually dressed. I said "hullo" to him. I suddenly felt slightly ill at ease because I had been sent to ask him for money. I shouted at the top of my voice with my eyes on the ground. It had started to rain heavily.

"My father sent me here to ask you for five thousand pounds!"

"There's no need to shout," he replied. "Who is your father and what does he want the money for?"

"Who is your father and what does he want the money for?"

"For the anti-airport campaign," I said.

Then I made the mistake of looking him in the eye. His eyes were light hazel in colour. They were almost golden. He was so extraordinarily good-looking that I fainted.

When I came round, I was in a spare bedroom which had twin beds. Betty came into the room, carrying a tray of tea.

"What happened?" I asked.

"There's no need to worry. You were outside in the drive, talking to Bob in the pouring rain, without a mackintosh. He said you looked cold and white before you fell."

I then realized where I was and why I was there. Betty very kindly said I could stay at Headington Hill Hall any time I wanted to. I told her about Mr Brightwell, and his insistence on watching *Dad's Army*. I also told her how angry he would be if he missed it.

After about twenty minutes, Bob came into the room.

"I know about your Dad owning *The Daily Telegraph*, but I don't know anything about you as a person. What are your interests?" he asked.

"The Russian language, Russian folk songs, Russian literature and the Communist Party."

"Are you a member of the Communist Party?"

"Yes."

"What made you join?"

"I was influenced by Gorki's novel, *The Mother*."

"Have you ever been to Russia?"

"Yes, I went there last year."

"Who with?" Bob asked suddenly.

"I went alone. I didn't tell my parents I was going there, as they said I couldn't go. Not only did they disapprove of my going there. The idea of going there alone was an anathema to them. I told them I was going away for a few days, to stay with some friends in Cornwall."

"Go on."

"I'm afraid they found out that I had gone to Moscow, unaccompanied."

"How?" asked Bob.

"Well, a man called Frank Taylor, *The Daily Telegraph*'s Moscow correspondent, rang my father up and told him I was sitting in his office, having asked him if he personally could put me up in his flat for another month. He told my father he was very embarrassed because he feared I was trying to defect, i.e. to become a Soviet citizen. I went back to London in disgrace."

"Why did you lie to us?" asked my mother.

"Because I didn't want you to know the truth," I replied.

Bob laughed.

"Do you speak Russian?" he asked.

"Yes. My parents wouldn't let me learn the language, so I taught myself."

"Do you mean you had no lessons?"

"No. You can always learn something if you really want to."

"I've never seen such guts!" said Bob, "and yet, you're scared of your driver's rage if he misses bloody *Dad's Army*."

Bob spoke to me in Russian. I was able to reply and was very pleased with myself.

"I regard you as a surrogate daughter," he said. "However, it's time you got up. Then we can have tea downstairs, and I will write out a cheque for your Dad. Perhaps your driver would like to have tea with us. What's his name?"

"Mr Brightwell."

"Mr Lightweight – did you say?"

I had uncontrollable giggles.

"What's so funny?"

"No. It's Brightwell, not Lightweight."

Mr Brightwell was sitting in my father's Ford. He was smoking and looking at a picture of a naked woman in one of the tabloids.

Bob knocked peremptorily on his window. I must point out that he related more easily to women than to members of his own sex, so his handling of the peppery Mr Brightwell was the opposite of the way he treated me.

"You there, sitting in a bloody hearse, looking at a picture of a naked woman," he boomed, as if Mr Brightwell were sitting fifty yards away. "What's taken your fancy?"

An expression of rage clouded over Mr Brightwell's face and his eyes almost came out of their sockets. I got the giggles once more.

"Mind your own flippin' business, sir!" he shouted, adding furiously, "This is not an 'earse. It's a Ford Estate."

"What's your name?" asked Bob, although I had already told him.

"Harry Brightwell."

"I'd like you to come to my house and have tea with my wife and me, Mr Brightwell" said Bob, in a commanding tone of voice.

Mr Brightwell fanatically took off his cap and put it back on again. He put out his cigarette.

"I'll 'ave you know that I've been serving the Berry family, and the Smith family before that!" he shouted, adding, "It was my privilege to groom Lord Birkenhead's[1*] 'orses!"

"Bugger what you did to Lord Birkenhead's horses!" said Bob impatiently. "Get out of your vehicle and join us for tea. Eleanor

---

[1*] Lord Birkenhead, better known as "F. E. Smith", was the author's maternal grandfather. Barrister, wit, statesman, Lord Chancellor and Secretary of State for India, he died in 1930, long before the author was born.

said you were keen on *Dad's Army.*" (Bob sometimes referred to cars as "vehicles". It was part of his eccentricity.)

Mr Brightwell threw his paper onto the floor. He got out of the car, very hesitantly, glaring at Bob as he moved. He walked slowly into the house with his head lowered, as if he were walking behind his mother's coffin.

Bob led us into an airy room, containing Empire furniture, a harp and a grand piano. He introduced Mr Brightwell to Betty, who offered him some cake which she had baked herself but which he refused. She gave him a cup of tea while he sat nervously on the edge of his chair.

Bob asked Mr Brightwell a few questions, which were delivered with the arresting and startling intonation characteristic of him, and was answered with monosyllables. I was unable to work out whether Mr Brightwell's answers were due to uncharacteristic reticence, anger or fear of missing *Dad's Army*.

Bob turned to his wife. "When does *Dad's Army* start, Betty?" he asked her.

"In about fifteen minutes' time. I think it's on BBC 2."

"Good. Our guest likes it and would like to watch it. You'll stay and watch it with us, won't you, Mr Brightwell?" said Bob.

Mr Brightwell appeared even more nervous than before.

"I can't stay, sir," he said. "Eleanor's father will be wanting her back."

We all got up. Mr Brightwell walked out of the house first.

Bob ushered me aside and put a sealed envelope containing his cheque, into my hand.

"Blimey! That driver of yours is a scary fellow! I wouldn't like to meet him alone on a dark night," he remarked.

I got the giggles once more.

"It doesn't take much to get you going," said Bob, "You're a bit batty, you are."

I said, "Goodbye" to Betty and thanked Bob for the cheque. I got into my father's car. On the way home, I tried to break what had become a stony silence between Mr Brightwell and myself.

"What did you think of Mr Maxwell, Mr Brightwell?" I ventured.

Mr Brightwell changed gear, grinding the clutch. "No comment!" he barked.

* * *

It was seven o'clock by the time I got home. My mother was upstairs. My father was sitting by the fire waiting for me.

"What took you so long?" he asked.

"I found Bob so ravishingly good-looking today, that I fainted. I had to be put to bed for a while."

"Cor, love a duck!" said my father obscurely. "Have you got the money?"

"Yes." I handed him the sealed envelope and he opened it.

"This cheque is made out for a sum of money, which is cheekily short of the five thousand pounds,[2*] which I asked you to get," he complained.

After dinner, I rang Bob up and thanked him for the tea and the cheque, although the latter had been made out for a modest sum of money, as my father had pointed out to me.

I was pleased because I had told Bob that I had joined the Communist Party, had taught myself Russian, against my parents' wishes, and had gone to Russia alone, having told them that I was going to stay with friends in Cornwall. I could tell that he was impressed.

* * *

I was rather unhappy during my late teens. I consulted quite a few psychiatrists, one of whom told me that I had paranoid

---

[2*] The author knows what Bob's cheque amounted to, but refuses to disclose the sum.

16

schizophrenia, simply because I lay down on his couch, forgetting to take off my overcoat, scarf and gloves. Bob was militantly opposed to me having seen the doctors.

One of the reasons for my unhappiness was that I was beginning to lose faith in the Communist Party. I was like a priest who had lost his belief in a Supreme Being.

I lost my faith in communism for a number of reasons. Firstly, I read accounts in the newspapers of Russian intellectuals being sent to labour camps, where they were tortured, because they had dared to criticize the communist regime.

Another unpleasant feature of communism, manifested itself during my visit to Moscow. I saw a play about the Russian Revolution, called "*Shestoi Illyoolia*".

When the actor, playing the part of Felix Derzhinsky, the evil head of Lenin's secret police, swaggered onto the stage, many starry-eyed members of the audience, rose to their feet, clapping and cheering. I found this horrifying.

There was another reason for my disillusionment with communism. In his Manifesto, Lenin had promised, "We will build gold latrines for the workers." None of the public lavatories I visited in Moscow were gold. Instead, they were made of off-colour, chipped enamel. Lenin, the Bolshevik "hero" had disgraced himself by breaking his promise.

Also, I read a militantly Left-wing magazine called *The Black Dwarf* on one occasion. Published in London, this magazine did not cover workers' rights or unacceptably low wages, as I had expected it to. Instead, it oozed vindictive, unadulterated hatred for anyone who failed to support its editorials. It advocated total dictatorship and was a Nazi paper.

The final straw, which broke the camel's back, where my loss of faith in communism was concerned, occurred during my visit to East Berlin, accompanied by my mother. I wondered whether Lenin had kept his promise in East Berlin, even if he had failed to keep it in Moscow.

I went to the lavatory at Checkpoint Charlie. I hoped in vain that everything would be made of gold. There was nothing gold about the place. When I pulled the chain, the ballcock came away in my hand and the tank crashed to the floor, flooding the whole cubicle and the corridor outside. Added to that, the lavatory was absolutely filthy.

My mother was sighing heavily and pacing up and down outside the lavatory. When I came out, she exclaimed: "It would be you, wouldn't it? Do you realize you've been and got the man out?"

I expected to see a single, mildly disinterested guard. Instead, I was met by three guards and a savage-looking Alsatian dog.

"These people will be sending the bill for the damage you've done, to the British Government!" said my mother, adding, "I can't take you anywhere, can I?"

On my return to London, I wrote a letter to the Communist Party's Head Office, in which I tendered my resignation.

* * *

Apart from my loss of faith in communism, there was something else causing me to be unhappy during my teens. I inherit my passion for the macabre, from my maternal aunt, the self-confessed gypsy author, Eleanor Smith, as well as from my maternal grandmother, who attended the trial of Crippen, when pieces of his wife's chopped up body were being passed from one jury member to another.

I threw myself into the study of pre-revolutionary Russian literature and its fatalistic tones. So fascinated was I by the moribund works of such writers as Max Gorki, Checkhov, Dostoevsky and others, that, for want of better words, I became hooked on the morbidity of these books.

I was at Wycombe Abbey at the time and in Wendover House.

My housemistress, Miss Donaldson, knew the affairs and minds of everyone in her house, like the back of her hand. She took me aside one evening and summoned me to her study. She always wore shabby Oxfam dresses and had cropped grey hair. Overall she looked like an ageing lesbian. "You thought you could possess Russian literature, didn't you?" she said. You haven't been able to do so. It has possessed you. Give it up while you can. The books you've been reading contain references to grim times. If you continue to read them, you will become mentally ill."

How I wished I had listened to her!

So obsessed was I that I couldn't stop reading Russian books. I ignored her and thought she was rather a crank.

Eventually, I had read so much that my mind had become temporarily damaged. I was sent to the school sanatorium for a few weeks. The sanitorium was very pleasant and its rooms were nice and airy.

I got on quite well with most of the girls there and talked to them at length about Russian literature. They were bored shitless. One night, I broke something open. It looked like a large tank in one of the bathrooms and I flooded the whole building. It was much later that I did roughly the same thing at Checkpoint Charlie.

A woman known as "Nurse Birch", who had a strong Yorkshire accent and a loud, commanding voice, stormed into the bathroom to see how much damage I had done.

"I found an extraordinary-looking contraption in here which exploded when I tampered with it," I ventured.

"There are *many* extraordinary-looking contraptions in here which explode when tampered with, and *I* am one of them!" shouted Nurse Birch.

I continued to read pre-revolutionary Russian novels while I was in the sanatorium. Instead of fascinating me, the books began to torture me in a very serious way. I was confined to bed with nothing to read, except *Just William*.

At a much later date, I told Bob about these really unpleasant experiences, including my reasons for resigning from the Communist Party.

On another subject altogether, before my loss of faith in communism and my preoccupation with nineteenth-century Russian literature, my mother arranged to meet me in *Aldo Bruno's*, an upmarket hairdresser's in Mayfair (London). The hairdresser's salon was in 22 Motcomb Street. It has since been closed down.

I went into the salon, carrying a bundle of rolled-up newspapers. The top newspaper on the pile was *The Daily Worker*, a communist paper.

I greeted my mother, sat down next to her and began to read it. Hairdressers stared at us, giggling. They knew that I was both annoying and embarrassing my mother.

She made a considerable amount of noise and expressed disgust on seeing me reading a communist newspaper in such smart surroundings. The salon was frequented on a daily basis by film stars, the aristocracy and Tory newspaper proprietors' wives, among others. Had my mother made less noise, she wouldn't have attracted so much attention to what I was reading.

Her voice was even louder and deeper than mine. She snatched *The Daily Worker* from my hands and waved it in the air.

"Where in the world did you get this?" she demanded.

"I bought it," I said proudly.

"Why did you buy it?"

"Because I like it."

"Why do you like it?"

"Why?" I said loudly, "I like its contents. I like its editorials and I like its reasoning."

Aldo Bruno, who owned the salon, allowed his mouth to gape open, like a goldfish about to bite the dust. He lacked a sense of humour. His scissors fell from his hand onto the floor.

"I can see *she* won't be coming here again," he said, disagreeably.

"You do see I have an awful lot to put up with," said my mother, her voice low, like that of a Catholic at confession.

It was when my mother and I were walking across the street to her car, with a parking ticket on its windscreen, that she began to take off. She spoke loudly enough to be heard in Bayswater, about farmers under Stalin being collectivized, and the horror of Soviet labour camps.

Dumbfounded passers-by formed a circle round us, to listen to her articulate condemnation of communism. Suddenly, she added, as an afterthought:

"Do you realize Lady Glendevon, the Marchioness of Salisbury and Lady Rothermere were all in there today? You've made a laughing stock of us both!"

My mother turned her embarrassment into a joke, later on, at a family gathering. Her narrative was distorted and surreal.

Disgruntled hairdressers were accounted for as fainting in droves. Even *imaginary* ambulances were described, screeching to a halt, their sirens blearing, before picking up traumatized aristocrats in curlers.

At that time, I was actually proud of being a communist.

"Do you mind if we have Robert Maxwell to lunch on Sunday?" asked Nicky, changing the subject. "I need to know why he wants to buy *The News of the World*".

"Certainly, not this Sunday," said my mother. "Adelaide Jesus will be in Barbados, attending a funeral then."

"Who the hell's Adelaide Jesus?" asked Nicky.

"She's the cook. Don't you know that?"

"I've often seen a woman working in the kitchen, but I had no idea she had a wacky name like Adelaide Jesus," said Nicky.

"Adelaide Jesus is no stranger a name than Nicholas Berry!" said my mother angrily.

"Can't we hire someone else while she's away?"

"That's not possible. All we've got is Dot Jenkins, a seventy-two-year-old dear who's just about capable of boiling an egg." said my mother, adding obscurely, "One can't give Robert Maxwell a boiled egg for lunch. He's so peculiar and sensitive,

21

he might totally misconstrue the situation! Get the man over on Sunday week."

I was intrigued by my mother's use of the words "the man". It was as if she were referring to a plumber, or someone of that ilk.

"All right. I'll ring him up later," said Nicky. "Perhaps I could ask him whether he would like a boiled egg!"

"Shut your trap!" exclaimed my mother.

* * *

The following Sunday, Bob came to our house in Buckinghamshire for lunch, minus Betty, but with his twin daughters, Isabel and Christine. He turned up, wearing a fur hat and a trench-like overcoat. He was looking very attractive. He sat next to my mother and I sat on his other side.

He turned to me, to bring me into the conversation.

"Are you keen on opera?" he asked.

"Some operas, yes. *Carmen*'s my favourite. I also like *La Traviata* and *The Magic Flute*," I replied.

"I admire the extent of your knowledge. Are you interested in politics at all?"

"She's a communist, you know. She needs to read *The Daily Worker* every day, just as a Chinaman needs rice," said my mother.

"I know she's a communist," said Bob, "She told me so herself."

"Also, she's a card-carrying member of the Communist Party," continued my mother. "She takes bouquets of flowers to the Russian Embassy every year on Lenin's birthday." My mother added her favourite words, "I do have an awful lot to put up with."

Bob looked at me approvingly, as he did on most occasions. Perhaps, he thought I was eccentric and had a *penchant* for eccentric young women.

"Your Eleanor's got amazing guts," said Bob to my mother.

22

"Yes, she's a plucky little thing," my mother replied.

* * *

My disillusionment with communism and the effect that love of moribund slav literature had on me, were not the only causes of my contact with the medical profession during my teens. My compulsory hospitalization was brought about by the following trivial incident:

A mentally disturbed friend of mine, called Peter van Praagh[3*] gave me a gold pill-box for my birthday. I decided to have something engraved on it. There is an old Russian folk song, whose chorus is interchangeable with English words:

"Nye zhivoi v styeppi, chellovyek lezhit.
Okolo myotvovo voron kruzhit."

(These words are in Cyrillic letters, of course.)
The English words of the chorus are:
"In the steppe a dead man lies.
Round the man a raven flies."

I went to a jeweller's shop, then at Paddington Station. The scruffy, unshaven man standing behind the counter was unattractive and unnecessarily unfriendly. I would have got the job done somewhere else, but I was in a hurry to catch a train to Oxford, to stay with the Maxwells for the weekend.

I handed the jeweller a piece of paper, on which the English words of the song were printed. I told him succinctly that the word *"steppe"* was not spelt *"step"* but *"steppe"*. I went out of my way to emphasize this point, and told him that I would be returning to collect the pill-box, in half an hour's time.

3* Peter van Praagh was a dear friend of mine. He had bi-polar tendencies and a history of violence towards his wife. He was my model for Joseph Slandisch in *Your Father Had to Swing, You Little Bastard!* He took his life in March 1988, but had the courtesy and the loyalty to buy fifteen copies of *Never Alone with Rex Malone* first.

I came back to the shop within half an hour, and I asked the man for my property and also for the price of the engraving.

"That will be thirty pounds," he said.

To my horror, he had engraved the word "*step*", as opposed to "*steppe*". I assumed that he had deliberately spelt the word incorrectly for some perverse reason. I slapped him. Then I was verbally abusive towards him and I told him I would not be paying him. I moved towards the door which he had locked from the inside.

He called the police. Two officers turned up. He told the policemen his side of the story, exaggerating throughout. He presented himself as being efficient, reasonable and pleasant. As I had hit him, and had been verbally abusive towards him as well, I was "slung down the nick". Finally, I was "sectioned" and two psychiatrists were sent for. I do not wish to bore my readers by going into detail.

The two psychiatrists eventually turned up and signed a bogus document to indicate that I was "mentally ill". I was also under-age.

Finally, I was incarcerated in an obscure, psychiatric hospital. Two nurses held me steady while a needle was pushed into my arm. I had been injected with a substance called "chlorpromazine", which induces severe depression and, if used extensively, can turn patients into vegetables.

A nurse took my details. I said that my parents were dead. I did not wish them to be informed that I had been violent, for fear of being cut out of their wills. I gave Nicky's name and phone number and said he was my next of kin.

I have always hated nurses. If any woman puts on a nurse's uniform she turns into Hitler.

Among the loathsome side-effects of chlorpromazine are hallucinations. When I opened a drawer in my tiny cubicle, I saw a decapitated baby in it. When I went to the bathroom, I saw a hanged man covered in blood. His face looked like Nicky's. I screamed my head off.

One of the nurses managed to get in touch with Nicky, and gave him the name and address of the mental hospital in which I had been incarcerated. He came to see me. I overheard him shouting at the senior psychiatrist who had sectioned me. His name was "Dr" Morgan Whitteridge. I heard Nicky's furious words, "My name is Nicholas Berry. My family are very powerful and could have you relieved of your responsibilities. They could also bring your hospital to a complete standstill, if you don't stop persecuting my sister."

Whitteridge came into my cubicle and said, "Nicholas Berry does not run this hospital."

"Pity!" I said, adding, "You're a filthy conman!"

Nicky came back to see me every day for about a week. The chlorpromazine increased my misery which had become so severe, that I had to be given electric shock treatment or E.C.T. Whitteridge had been a "pioneer of" electric shock treatment. He told me that it would ease my misery, caused by the chlorpromazine, which I shouldn't have been given at all.

I'm told electric shock therapy is no longer used in England, because it is so dangerous. It causes a condition, known as "catatonia". This means that the patient is unable to move, speak or stand up. The treatment was first used in mental hospitals order to replace straitjackets.

Bob rang Nicky up from the phone in his Rolls, shortly after I had been due to stay at Headington Hill Hall. Using very fruity language, he demanded to know why I had stood him up.

Nicky explained the situation and said my condition had deteriorated. He gave Bob the address of the hospital.

"Who's her fucking GP?" asked Bob, who automatically assumed that my GP had been controlling the two bent psychiatrists.

"A certain Dr Carl Heinz Goldman, whose rooms are at number one, Upper Wimpole Street, London W1." Nicky gave Bob Dr Goldman's phone number.

Dr Goldman (now deceased) was a well-known figure, who kept a high profile in the private medical community. He was devastatingly attractive and spoke with a seductive Leipzig accent. He was a compulsively randy rake about town. He was Jewish and had fled Germany during the Third Reich. He had had a number of love affairs, and his wife had left him twice. This had caused him agonizing melancholia.

He was moody, passionate and hot-tempered. He has appeared in some of my books, under the name of "Dr Sergei Festenstein". Because he is a recurrent character, I never kill him.

Mistakenly, Bob stormed into Goldman's consulting room, while a half-naked woman lay on his leather-studded consulting couch. He recognized Bob straight away, from his photographs in the newspapers.

"Get out of my consulting room, you crook!"

"You're killing Eleanor Berry, you quack!"

Goldman had called Maxwell a crook and Maxwell had called Goldman a quack.

"They were both right," commented an odious Sloane Ranger, after the much talked-about, fiery row between the two East-European sex sirens. Both Goldman and Maxwell came to me independently, and complained bitterly about the other. Also, each one asked me if I were in love with the other. This happened after my release from the hospital.

I absolutely adored the row which I heard about later. I was falling all over the place, I was laughing so much. During the row, Bob had told Goldman that he knew "fuck all" about mental illness and that his (Bob's) encyclopaedias were awash with information about the subject. Very regrettably, Bob had been attacking the wrong person, when it was Whitteridge who had been in charge of the electric shock therapy, not Goldman.

The following has nothing to do with my relationship with Bob, but the matter in hand but it is worth mentioning. I once seriously blotted my copy book in the corridor outside Goldman's consulting room.

I saw a woman whom I thought was a new receptionist. Because I was in a disinhibited frame of mind, I went up to her and said, "My God, that man, Goldman, is attractive. He must come like the Volga!"

"Kindly keep your opinion to yourself and wait in the waiting room, if you don't mind!" said the woman aggressively.

I approached Goldman's secretary.

"Who is that disagreeable new receptionist?" I asked. "Is she an agency temp?"

"No, she isn't," replied the secretary. "She is Dr Goldman's wife."

Bob was extremely amused by my Goldman stories. In a way, it is possible that he regarded the fiery doctor as his rival. Goldman could be quite violent and was not averse to hitting other doctors.

My father, who had just had a hip replacement, had been consulting another doctor, Dr Creightmore, whom Goldman referred to disdainfully as "the locum."

There was a bottle of whisky on my father's bedside table in his room in the London Clinic.

Goldman came into the room, where he found Creightmore and seized the bottle of whisky.

He gave Creightmore a resounding slap on the ear.

"How dare you allow him this, you brainless nincompoop, when I've just saved his liver!" he shouted.

* * *

Bob was driven to the mental hospital by his driver, Mr Hoppitt. That wasn't his nickname. It was his real name. He did not take offence easily, and had a sense of humour, which is why Bob had employed him for so many years.

Bob liked him to drive fast and Hoppitt must have screeched to a halt outside the hospital, judging by the skid marks in the gravel.

Bob entered the hospital, wearing a white, flannel suit and a coalminer's cloth cap. I had just been wheeled into the operating theatre, while Whitteridge was preparing to give me yet another anaesthetic before the electric shock treatment was due to start.

Somehow, Bob had found his way to the operating theatre, and had rattled straight in without getting scrubbed up. Whitteridge had put electrodes onto my head, and one of his minions was about to turn on the current. I pleaded with him not to do so but he ignored me. I was *compos mentis* enough to recognize Bob. One of Whitteridge's helpers was awaiting instructions from his boss. Two medics, shrouded in gowns, gaped at Bob in astonishment.

"How dare you come in here, when you're not scrubbed up!" one of them said, his voice raised.

"Turn that fucking machine off!" shouted Bob.

The staff in the operating theatre, including Whitteridge, were mesmerized. Bob extended his hand and lifted me. He carried me out of the operating theatre. I was able to direct him to my cubicle and got dressed while he waited in the corridor.

If I had had so much as one more treatment, I would have become a vegetable. Effectively, Bob saved my life.

He led me to the Rolls and eased me into the back, as I couldn't walk very well. He got into the passenger's seat. No-one prevented him from taking me away from the hospital. No-one dared because of who he was. I looked at him in wonder.

"Yea though I walk through the valley of the shadow of death, I will fear no evil, for thou art with me and thy rod and thy staff comfort me," I said.

"Shut up!" shouted Bob. "I don't want to have a load from the Scriptures thrown at me."

A number of factors caused Bob's actions to be entirely legal. Firstly, Whitteridge's junior partner, Dr Pearce, was unqualified to practice. It was later found out that he had asked one of his friends to sit his Finals for him. The so-called "friend" blackmailed him, shortly after my incarceration. Dr Pearce surrendered and parted with approximately ten thousand pounds.

Secondly, hitting someone, who has damaged property, is not a severe enough offence to merit being sectioned. I just happened to be with the wrong crowd at the wrong time. If I had got a lawyer, it would have caused my name to appear in the newspapers, and would have led to my being cut out of my parents' wills.

"Floor it, Hoppitt," said Bob. Head for Oxford."

Mr Hoppitt's speed was unacceptable in Bob's eyes. The tycoon hit his driver on the back of the head with a rolled-up copy of *The Financial Times*, but thought better of what he had done.

"Oh, I was just swatting a fly, Hoppitt," he said.

Mr Hoppitt increased his speed to 55 m.p.h. in a 30 m.p.h. zone.

He was beckoned to the side of the road by the driver of a panda car. He was on his own.

"Get out of your car, please, sir," he said. He had a regional accent.

Mr Hoppitt did as he was told and took a breathalyser test which was negative. This took time. Bob eased himself into the driver's seat. "Sorry, sir," he said. "My driver's lost the way. You'll have to sort this out with him."

Bob drove off, leaving Mr Hoppitt by the roadside with the police officer. My hero worship of Bob increased. As Max Gorki said about Tolstoy, Bob was truly God-like.

During the journey to Oxford, Bob reprimanded me for having allowed myself to be sectioned. Also, there was some chlorpromazine in my system, which had made me staggeringly slow-witted.

"You should never have allowed these shits to take you to a mental hospital in the first place," he said, adding, "Your recovery will be slow because, now that you've used that crutch, you'll take a long time to learn to walk again."

"None of this was my fault, Bob", I said.

"You're wrong. Pussycat. It was entirely your fault. You attacked a man at Paddington Station – Douglas someone or other, his name is, apparently. You went on, telling him the difference between 'steppe' and 'step'." Bob spelt out the two words. "It's true, the man may have been a fucking idiot, but it was silly of you to slap him."

I didn't feel like talking, even to Bob. I was exhausted because of the chlorpromazine, which was still in my system.

"Yes, Bob," I said with lamb-like meekness.

There was a long silence.

"I've got good news for you," he said eventually.

"Oh, yes?"

"Your brother, Nicholas, is coming to dinner tonight. That should cheer you up. Also, I'm going to tackle this man, Whitteridge. I made a mistake when I had it out with that Goldman fellow."

"All right, Bob," I said. I went to sleep and didn't wake up until we arrived at Headington Hill Hall.

* * *

Betty came into the hall and greeted us. Bob was tired. Betty asked me what had been happening, and said she had been very worried by my failure to turn up for the weekend. I answered her question. My grammar was atrocious.

"Nurse gave me terrible injection. Also, they gave me electric shock treatment. Bob came into operating theatre and told psychiatrist to turn off current."

"Why aren't you using the definite article?" asked Bob in an exasperated tone of voice.

Later, Nicky came to dinner and generated a cheerful atmosphere in the diningroom. The conversation was mainly about high finance, though, a subject I know nothing about.

I felt a bit better the following morning. However, my recovery was a hard slog. It took several days for the chlorpromazine to disappear from my system completely.

The following morning, the Maxwells were having breakfast in the kitchen. I had joined them. Nicky had left after dinner the night before. Bob took a phone call from Rome. He was on the phone for about fifteen minutes.

"What's going on in Rome?" I asked inanely.

"Rome stands where Rome stood, on the Tiber," he replied.

Some of the Maxwell children were staying in the house. They were all very friendly towards me. My favourite is Ian. I like him because he is dynamic, like his father, and also very jolly.

He always encourages me by saying things like, "Don't worry. You're not going to fall over," on occasions when I have had a few too many. He also likes to talk about his father. He is a mine of information about Bob's deprived childhood. What'smore, he looks rather like his father.

* * *

It was a Saturday. Ian had been working with Bob in the offices of Pergamon Press which were up a hill, near a main road. He (Ian) came into the drawingroom and offered me a drink.

"I always have to jump to attention when the Good Lord calls," he said, in jest. "With Dad, it's just work, work, work and nothing else. You may not understand this but I really am very fond of the old bugger!"

I had a long conversation with Isabel who is the same age as me. We were in the sauna. She told me a rather bizarre story about her father. She said she had once told him she was going to the Maxwell bookshop in Oxford, "to have a look around". She was fifteen years old at the time. Incidentally, Bob had very kindly told me I could go to his bookshop whenever I wanted to, and put

31

anything I decided to buy, onto his account. If that's not kindness and generosity, I don't know what is.

Isabel told me she had gone to the bookshop, where she had bumped into a young man whom she had fancied. The man shared a pot of tea with her and they exchanged addresses. When she returned home, Bob called her into his study.

"Was there something you wanted, Daddy?" she asked.

"Yes. Go over there and sit down."

Isabel did so.

"You told me you were going to the bookshop to have a look around, but you went there in order to meet a young man, didn't you?" said Bob confrontationally.

"I only bumped into him by chance, Daddy. I didn't expect to see him there."

Bob looked sternly at his daughter.

"I don't believe you. I am disappointed in you, Isabel. You have deceived your father," he said.

I hate to say this, but I thought Bob's conduct was veering towards the unreasonable on this occasion. However, we all have our faults, don't we?

"That's a weird story," I said. I climbed down from the top bench to ladle more cold water onto the coals onto my body.

"Surely, you couldn't have taken that incident too seriously," I said. "Perhaps, your father was over-reacting. Someone must have seen you and given a misleading impression to your father. Maybe, he didn't quite understand what had happened."

"I felt dreadful about it for several months." said Isabel.

"Several months? You get over a trivial incident like that within about a week," I said.

Isabel seemed resentful.

"You don't understand. I felt my father wouldn't trust me any more."

"Very few people trust me, but I don't get into a state about it for several months," I said.

32

"My father can be really autocratic at times," said Isabel, adding, "Once, Anne, Phillip and I had gone to the cinema in Headington. My father asked them to put a notice on the screen, demanding that we all go home immediately.

"I wouldn't have gone," I said.

There was a pause.

"Was your father very strict with you?" asked Isabel.

"My father was and still is very kind. He is stern and was stern in the past, particularly if any of us disobeyed him."

"If my father had told me to do something, I would have done whatever he'd told me to do, straight away. Were you very naughty when you were little?"

"Yes, I was." I replied. "I poured a handful of gravel into my father's driver's bowl of clean oil. The oil was due to go into my father's car. My parents made me learn, *The Charge of the Light Brigade* by heart as a punishment. My mother even suggested that I should go to the driver's cottage and recite it to him on his doorstep, but my father said this wouldn't be fair on the driver," because of my monotonous and deep voice."

I got to know Isabel quite well. She wrote to me after I had sent her a copy of *Never Alone with Rex Malone*, which was a fantasy about her father's alleged relationship with a crooked, over-sexed funeral director.

She wrote, "Thank you for sending me a copy of your book. I found it very disturbing and macabre. However, you have treated my parents interestingly and kindly, so I thank you for that."

Isabel and I continued to pour water over ourselves. She told me about her boyfriends. "Have you ever been in love?" she asked suddenly.

Her question jolted me a little. "I'm in love with two older men," I said.

"What? At the same time?" she asked.

"Yes, that can happen." I was referring to Bob and Dr Goldman but, for obvious reasons, I couldn't tell Isabel this.

"What are they like, the two men?" she asked. She was fascinated, too fascinated for my liking.

"One of them is sixty-five and the other is forty-seven."

"The forty-seven year old sounds more suitable than the sixty-five year old. A sixty-five year old could easily collapse on top of you and die of a heart attack during the sex act."

I laughed, although I was beginning to feel uneasy.

"Do tell me about the forty-seven-year-old. Is he good-looking? My Dad's forty-seven as well," said Isabel.

"Yes," I ventured.

"Can't you tell me any more? Do you think I would like him if I met him?"

"That's the most difficult question I've ever been asked in my life!" I replied.

"You *are* mad. Do tell me about him. Does he work?"

"Yes. He works," I said reluctantly. I wished Isabel would change the subject but she didn't.

"What does he do?" she asked.

I said the first thing that came into my head.

"Oh, he writes novels."

"Is he like my father in any way?" asked Isabel.

"It's very hot in here. I'm beginning to feel faint. I'm going for a swim," I said assertively.

"I'll come with you," said Isabel. "I promise I won't talk to you any more about the man of forty-seven, because I can tell, you feel embarrassed whenever you talk about him, for some reason. Just two more questions, though. Then I'll shut up. Are the two men married?"

"Yes," I said in a rather snappy tone of voice.

"Have you been to bed with either of them?"

I got very irritable, "No, I fucking well haven't!"

"Would you like to go to bed with the forty-seven year old?"

I sat on the edge of the pool. Isabel joined me.

"I know how much you hate this topic of conversation, Ellie, but... " began Isabel.

"I certainly do. You're so right!"

"OK. I'll ask you one more question, and then I promise I'll shut up."

"What the hell's your next question?"

"Have either of these men expressed a desire to go to bed with you?"

"Nope!" I said, my voice raised. I stood up and dived into the water.

When I got out of the water, I dressed in the hut and went into the house. Isabel had already reached the house. She was a faster walker than I was.

"I'm sorry if I upset you Ellie," she said, adding, "It's typical of English people to hold their cards close to their chests, and to resent it if someone looks over their shoulders."

"That's all right Izzy," I said, adding graciously, "I just can't bear talking about the two men I'm in love with. Neither of them would like me to do so, although my relationship with them both is entirely platonic."

Isabel smiled.

"It was awful of me to pry like that. I promise I won't do it again. Let's go into the kitchen and see if Mummy needs a hand," she said kindly.

I have always liked Isabel. She has got a sweet and very natural personality.

We went into the kitchen. Anne, one of the elder children, was peeling potatoes. Betty had gone into another room. Isabel's twin sister, Christine was sitting, on a rocking chair, reading *The Lord of the Rings*. Although the twins looked identical, they had different personalities. Isabel was rather serious. Christine, on the other hand, was light-hearted and liked to crack jokes all the time.

I introduced myself to Anne, whom I had never met before.

"What are you doing in life, Anne?" I asked.

"I want to be an actress. That is after I've got my degree. My father says I can't study drama before I graduate. I'm at university at the moment.

"Which university?"

"Lady Margaret Hall. That's in Oxford."

"What are you reading?" I asked.

"Modern Languages."

"Do you get on with your father?" I ventured.

Anne was taken aback by my question. I regretted having asked her.

"I'm close to my father. We all love him. I'm proud of him and of all the things he did during the War," she said stiltedly, adding, "It's true he's very strict and can be overbearing at times. He makes us work hard, so that we can excel later on in life. Whenever I have a problem, provided it's not a woman's problem, he's strong and supportive. He doesn't spoil any of us, except Ghislaine who's the youngest. He spoils her something rotten."

"Ghislaine?" I said. "I haven't met her yet."

"She's staying with a friend at the moment. She should be back any time now. I don't know whether you know this or not. My elder brother, Michael, was in a coma for some years, following a road accident. He and I were very close. Ghislaine was born three days after Michael's accident."

"I'm so sorry," I said. "Your father told me the tragic news about Michael, at his birthday party."

Anne continued, "My brother was coming home after a party. He was a passenger in a car which collided with another vehicle. This is not known, but it is suspected that either the driver of the car, or the driver of the other vehicle, was inebriated. As soon as Ghislaine was born, my parents thought she was a gift from Heaven. She's nine now – nine and naughty."

The following day, Ghislaine came back from her friend's house. We were all in the drawingroom. Ghislaine was wearing blue jeans, tennis shoes and a white T-shirt. She clambered onto her father's knee and put her arms round his neck. She had large brown eyes and brown hair, taken back in a ponytail. She was very pretty. While she was on her father's knee, I became agonizingly jealous of her.

"Who's this woman, Daddy?" she asked.

"That's very rude," said Bob. "You're supposed to say, 'My name is Ghislaine. I don't think we've met before.'"

The nine-year-old repeated her father's words.

"I'm Eleanor. I am a friend of your parents. It's nice to meet you," I said, a trifle stiffly.

We shook hands.

Bob had given Ghislaine a pony for her last birthday. She posed no threat to him, at that time, because she had favoured horses, before she had discovered men. Later on in her life, Bob had been profoundly jealous of her many boyfriends.

Someone had left the gate of the tennis court open, and her pony was wandering about on the court, and had left mounds of dung everywhere. It had also eaten its way through the net.

I had been walking with Bob in the garden. Ghislaine was lying on her back on the grass, outside the tennis court, with her legs bent, playing *God Save The Queen* on a recorder[4*].

"What's your pony doing on the tennis court?" Bob asked mildly.

At first, he was quite cross, but when he saw me laughing, his anger subsided.

He continued, "It's not that I mind your pony being on the tennis court, but I can't tolerate it if it leaves its visiting card behind."

Bob went back to the offices of Pergamon Press and left me alone with Ghislaine. We talked for a while. Though very cheeky, there was a natural sweetness and innocence about her. She told me she was due to receive a hiding from Bob that afternoon.

"What did you do to annoy him?" I asked.

"I asked Judy and Jean[5*] to do a job for me."

[4*] Recorder: A flute-like instrument

[5*] Judy Ennels, a senior secretary and Jean Baddeley (PA to Bob). Both these ladies are deceased.

"Who are Judy and Jean, and what did you ask them to do?"

"Oh, they are secretaries," said Ghislaine vaguely, adding, "I told them to organize the transport of various horses."

"What do you mean?" I asked.

"I said the horses were to be taken from Oxford to Basingstoke, for a point-to-point." (Whatever that is). "Then I asked these women to arrange for the horses to be brought back to Oxford afterwards."

"Did the two women say they were happy to carry out your orders?" I asked.

"Oh, yes. I told them my father had said it was all right."

"*Had* he said it was all right?"

"No," she said. She lowered her head and blushed.

"You're a very naughty girl. How old are you?"

"Nine."

I know I shouldn't have asked a nine-year-old child the next question, but I was absolutely riveted. I tried to hide the obsessive tone in my voice.

"When you said your father is going to give you a 'hiding,' what sort of a hiding will it be?" I asked as casually as I could.

Ghislaine looked nonplussed, as if she were thinking that she didn't deserve to be punished.

"Come with me into the house and I'll show you. There's a whole row of things on a table. Daddy always allows me to choose what I prefer to be beaten with." Ghislaine guided me to an empty room, which had probably been an office at some time.

I was fascinated by the sight of the punitive instruments, which had been arranged in a row on the table. Among the things I noticed, were a riding crop, a ruler, a stick, a cane, which made a swishing noise, on being brought down through the air, and a shoe horn which couldn't inflict any pain at all.

I regret that I was behaving very irresponsibly by toying with the psyche of a child. I laid my hand gently on her shoulder.

"Which one will *you* choose?" I asked, bending over backwards not to sound unhealthy or intimate.

"I'm going to choose the shoe horn. The shoe horn doesn't hurt," she replied.

"Indeed?" I said, "Does your father beat you with your trousers on or off?"

"On," said Ghislaine.

I was temporarily lost for words.

"Cor, love a duck, says I," I said eventually, copying one of my father's expressions.

"What does that mean?" asked the nine-year-old girl.

"Oh, nothing in particular."

She picked up the shoe horn.

"If I ask Daddy to use the shoe horn, I'll hardly feel a thing," she said.

"I know. You've just told me that".

There was a short silence. Ghislaine became rather cross for some reason.

"Which one would *you* choose, Eléanore, if my father wanted to beat you?" she asked.

"Well, Ghislaine, I personally would choose the cane, the one which is held high in the air, and which makes a swishing noise as it is brought down – Oh, sorry. I didn't mean to give you any funny ideas. Try to forget what I said just then!"

There was another silence. The child looked puzzled. I completely lost my head.

"I would ask your father if I could lower my trousers. Then I would ask him to whip me with the cane," I said.

"What? On your bare bottom?"

"Yes," I said, without thinking. I had caught a bit of sunstroke that morning and my wits were not about me.

"Why would you ask my father to beat you on your bare bottom with the cane, particularly when the cane is the most painful of the lot? You're not making any sense."

It was at this point that I got scared, as I feared that Ghislaine would repeat my words to her father.

"Well, Ghislaine," I replied, "Pain affects different people in different ways. If it were a man whipping me, I would only want him to be your father."

It seemed as if the child were giving me enough conversational rope to hang myself with. I was suddenly ashamed of my criminally tactless questions and answers.

"What are you talking about, Eléanore," asked Ghislaine.

My fear of her speaking to her father about me increased.

"Tell me the truth," she said, adding, "Would you *really* want to be whipped by my father with your trousers down?"

The words, "Oh, Christ, yes!" were struggling to be released from my lips. Somehow, I managed to control myself.

I said, "You've been very naughty, Ghislaine. You gave instructions to your father's secretaries about the transport of some horses. You lied when you told these women that your father had given you permission to have them transported. It stands to reason that you should be punished, whether with a shoe horn, or any other instrument."

Ghislaine persisted like a dog gnawing at its favourite bone.

"I really didn't understand you, when you said you'd actually like to take your trousers down and be whipped by my father."

I was getting even more nervous. There was another long silence. Finally, I managed to get my head out of the water.

"You may not know this, Ghislaine, but I am by no means perfect," I eventually managed to splutter. I added, "I've done dreadful things, worse even that what you did, and yet no-one has punished me. Hence, I am still guilty and I would like to be whipped by your father, just to get rid of my guilt."

I had really been sailing close to the wind. Now, I was talking bullshit.

"Why does it have to be my father who whips you, and no-one else?" persisted the exceptionally tiresome nine-year-old girl.

"Because I know him personally. I wouldn't want a total stranger to do it. Incidentally, we've been in this stuffy room for far too long. Let's go and sit on the lawn. There are other topics of conversation, besides the subject we have been discussing at exhaustive length. I'm beginning to find it an awful bore." I ventured.

I wonder, with a feeling of extreme guilt, whether I had warped Ghislaine's mind. She was surprised when I told her I wished to be beaten by her father, with the most painful of the instruments laid out.

At a much later date, when she had grown up, and had gone to live in New York, I was having lunch with Betty in her flat in London. I had consumed about three double gin and tonics and Betty very kindly said that I could lie down on the sofa and sleep them off. She was looking at her computer, which was in the same room as the sofa.

Quite unexpectedly, her land phone rang. Her phone was near her computer. Ghislaine was on the line.

It was about two o'clock in the afternoon in London, and breakfast time in New York.

I pretended to be asleep. I heard Betty comforting Ghislaine, as her daughter seemed upset about something.

"Are you seeing a psychiatrist about Daddy's canings when you were little?" asked Betty urgently. (Bob had died some years earlier.)

At the mention of the word "canings", I suddenly sat bolt upright. It was a reflex action.

"Ghislaine!" shouted Betty, sounding very alarmed. "I'm afraid we can't continue this conversation. Eléanore's here! She was asleep. Now, she's woken up! She's heard everything."

Betty reminded me a bit of Fagin[6*], when he was counting his tiaras. Oliver had woken up, after a deep sleep and was watching

---

6* Fagin: A leading character from Charles Dickens's novel, *Oliver Twist*.

him. He went berserk. I'm not saying that Betty actually went berserk but she was certainly very upset. Afterwards, I felt guilty about my invasion of his privacy. After all, I had always been devoted to her.

* * *

To revert to the past, Ghislaine showed me her pony, which was no longer on the tennis court. It was grazing in the long grass.

"Does your father ride?" I asked her.

"Not now, he doesn't, but just before he was given the M.C., he rode fearlessly into battle, on his jet black steed, flashing his sword in the shining sun!"

"You've got a rare gift for words," I said, adding, "Your father was a soldier and a brave one too. He didn't ride a horse on the battlefield. Incidentally, while I was walking past your father's offices, I saw a few secretaries with puppies in their rooms." (I can't tell you how relieved I was by the fact that we were no longer discussing corporal punishment!)

"Some of the secretaries have been given puppies. It was my father who gave them to the secretaries. Have you not seen the two golden Labradors, Tiger and Whisky?" asked Ghislaine.

"I know Tiger and Whisky," I said, "One is male; the other is female. Are they the parents of all the puppies?"

"Yes. We've got some puppies in the house as well."

"Whereabouts?"

"They're in a basket in a tiny area, next door to the kitchen."

"May I see them?"

"Yes. We'll go to the kitchen first, to see Mummy," said Ghislaine.

Betty and the Filipino cook, Oping, were alone in the kitchen. Ghislaine had run off. I introduced myself to Oping who always had a cheerful, smiling face.

"What have you been doing all morning?" asked Betty.

"I went for a walk with Bob and then I talked at some length to Ghislaine," I said guardedly.

"Ghislaine? She's in disgrace with Bob and me. Her behaviour has been quite appalling." I loved Betty's heavy French accent. I don't normally like French people, but she was an exception.

"Indeed? I heard something about horses," I said vaguely.

"I don't want to talk about that now. Come and sit beside me."

Oping continued Anne's work, peeling the potatoes. I started to wash the carrots. Betty talked to me about love, literature, philosophy and life.

What a magnificent mind she had! She showed supreme sensitivity when speaking about art, literature, music and many other subjects. She also had a phenomenal and touching vision of the importance of human kindness.

We spoke about Maupassant, Flaubert, Dostoevsky and Proust, among countless other literary figures.

I thought about my perverse conversation with Ghislaine once more. I hoped she didn't understand any of my questions and remarks. For a fleeting moment, I wondered whether I should confess my conduct to Betty. In the end, I decided I wouldn't.

Betty knew the many volumes of Proust's *À la Recherche du Temps Perdu* intimately. Later, at Sussex University, I was expected to read all the volumes in French, but I confess with shame that I only read a synopsis of them in English. I had to study Proust as a contextual course. My major subject was English. I get a terrible headache if I read things in French. I feel as if I've been sitting in a hot sun for a long time without a straw hat.

Betty spoke at length about Proust.

"The most wonderful thing about his works, is his attention to small details, which the human eye sometimes misses," she began.

"So many people take artistic things for granted. Those with too much money, who are unable to put their riches to intelligent use, become idle and self-pitying.

"Take stockbrokers' wives, for instance. They are forever sobbing into their gin and tonics, because they are incapable of setting themselves constructive occupational projects."

I smiled. I tried to imagine what a gin and tonic would taste like, were it to be laced with the tears of a discontented stockbroker's wife.

Betty continued and passed a saucepan of boiling water to Oping.

"Do you think that an empty-headed stockbroker's wife, or a débutante would notice some of the things which Proust noticed?" she asked. She continued, "I once read an intricate description by Proust of someone's balcony. He had described every inch of the fretwork in microscopic detail, even the shape of the beaks of the tiny bronze birds, intertwined with the railings."

The more Betty spoke about Proust's power of observation, the more ashamed I became of the questions I had asked Ghislaine. Betty obviously had an affinity for the rambling French writer, who, among other things, banged on and on about a crappy old biscuit.[7]* I, on the other hand, had been so influenced by Ghislaine's confessions, that I began to develop an affinity for the Marquis de Sade, the self-confessed flagellomaniac (otherwise known as the *Divine Marquis*), on whom I was later to do my thesis at university. My mother strongly disapproved of my decision.

Betty continued to speak passionately, "I feel that if all human beings could be capable of remembering beautiful objects, in the way Proust could, there would be less sadness in the world, except, of course, in the lives of the impoverished, the homeless and the bereaved. Have you read Keats's poem which begins with the words, "*No, no, go not to Lethe…*?"

"I know the one you're referring to," I said. "I had to write an essay about it when I was doing A' Level English. In comparison with you, I'm a dreadful Philistine, I'm afraid. When I'm down

---

7*   I have mentioned this matter in one of the anecdotes at the end of this book.

in spirits, I don't look at beautiful things. I go to the nearest pub where I get pissed."

Betty laughed. I was relieved by the fact that I hadn't shocked her.

"You really are a character!" she said, "That's what Bob likes so much about you."

As I said earlier, Betty was incapable of vindictiveness and jealousy. She was always exceptionally kind to me. She even got up early to drive me to the examination hall, to relax my nerves, when I was doing my A'Levels in English, French and Russian, before going to university.

She waited outside the examination hall, and took me out to lunch, to put me at my ease, before I sat my next paper. No-one else in the world would have done something as benevolent as that. Betty was a true saint and I am proud to have numbered her among my greatest friends.

I felt profoundly guilty because of my infatuation for her husband, however. I was relieved by the fact that he never made any sexual advances towards me, other than to stroke my cheek, hold onto my hair, hold my hand and kiss me briefly on the mouth.

"Ghislaine told me you had some puppies here," I said, "May I see them, please?"

"Why, yes! They're over here."

Six puppies, tiny enough to sleep in a grown man's shoe, played on a rug, surrounded by wire netting. Some of the puppies were golden; others were black.

Betty very kindly offered me a puppy, but I had to refuse the offer because of my unsuitable lifestyle.

As I went to the other part of the kitchen, I noticed a padlock on a door. It was on the door, leading to the larder.

"What's behind that door?" I asked.

"The larder. We have to lock it to keep Bob out, whenever we put him on a diet. Otherwise, he breaks in and eats everything there is. He broke in, only the other day, I'm sorry to say."

I listened, fascinated. Betty continued. "He ate a pound of cheese, a jar of peanut butter, two jars of caviar, a loaf of bread and a chicken in one go."

I struggled to keep a straight face.

"We had to change the lock," said Betty. "He broke the last one. Let's go next door and have a drink." I later learnt the reason for Bob's tendency to eat such large quantities of food. As a child, he had been racked by hunger all the time.

All the surviving Maxwell children were in the drawingroom. Bob, who had been working all morning, was standing behind the bar like a publican.

"What will you have, Missy?"

"Ginger beer, if you've got it," I replied.

"I haven't got it. Try something stronger."

"I'd like a gin and tonic then, please."

He gave me what I wanted. I took a few gulps. I felt a sense of euphoria as I stood, looking at Bob. The gin reached my stomach.

He came away from the bar and gave a spectacular wolf whistle. "Come on everyone, let's go and have lunch," he said.

The children stood up, as if they were responding to a military command. The family took their seats at the diningroom table from which there was a pleasant view of the lawn. I sat on Bob's right side. Jean Baddeley, his personal assistant and chief henchman, sat on his left side. She was the only person, apart from his tyrannical father, who was allowed to give him orders.

Oping passed food round the table. I took more potatoes than I thought I was going to eat. The dish was passed to Bob who took even more potatoes than I had taken.

Jean, who, incidentally, I have always liked very much, turned furiously to Oping.

"I thought I told you that Mr Maxwell was *not* to be offered potatoes!" she said angrily.

Jean took the serving spoon from Oping's hand, shovelled all the potatoes off the wretched man's plate, and put them back onto the serving dish. To my surprise, Bob said absolutely nothing and for a moment, I felt intensely jealous of the power that Jean appeared to wield over him.

I picked up some of my own potatoes with a desert spoon and put them onto his plate.

"I wouldn't stand for that, Bob!" I said. "Anyway, you're not fat, so there's no need for you to be on a diet."

"You *are* sweet!" he said. He stroked my cheek.

After lunch, Isabel, took me aside.

"Don't ever do that again, Ellie," she said. "My father has an eating problem and we all have to struggle to prevent him from harming himself."

"What do you mean? How could potatoes possibly harm him?" I asked.

Isabel lowered her voice.

"Once he starts to eat carbohydrates, he can't stop. Why else do you think we are locking him out of the larder? Do you know he's only got one lung?"

"Yes," I said. Isabel continued,

"His remaining lung has to do the work of two lungs. Extra strain is being put on his heart, if he eats too much. Jean and I have to break our backs keeping him healthy, and today, you undid precisely what we've been trying to do."

I couldn't understand what was going on at all. It was as if Isabel were speaking about an elderly, ailing dog, as opposed to a forty-seven-year-old, hot-blooded Cossack.

At the time, Bob was well-covered in an attractive sort of way, but he was not particularly fat. I realized, however, that the problem was none of my business.

"Sorry, Isabel. I won't do it again," I said.

I had been staying with the Maxwells for quite some time. One morning, I was having breakfast with the family in the kitchen when the phone rang. Bob answered it.

***

Although I have told the above anecdote in a fairly comical manner, the incident disturbed me greatly. I was particularly upset by the words "eating disorder" and by the fact that Jean and Isabel had gone out of their ways to ensure that Bob refrained from eating potatoes.

I was also distressed on hearing that he had a tendency to break into the larder and eat so much food, because he had been starved as a child.

I told some members of my family about the problem, although, in hindsight, I should not have done so.

"He does seem to be an awful Billy Bunter," commented my mother.

I had been staying with the Maxwells for quite some time. I was having breakfast with the family in the kitchen one morning, when the phone rang. Bob answered it.

My mother was on the line and asked to speak to me. Then she asked me why I had been away from home for so long. She said, in short, that I had been staying with the Maxwells for longer than the rules of hospitality permitted. She told me that she would be sending the legendary Mr Brightwell to collect me. She had a loud, carrying voice and the Maxwell family were able to hear every word she uttered.

"Pamela wants you back!" said Bob irritably. "I understand she's sending that scary old gnome over to pick you up."

That was what Bob used to call Mr Brightwell. Mr Brightwell, in turn, referred to Bob as "that 'orrible man up the 'all."

The reason I had been staying in Bob's house for such a long time, was that I had been thrown out of the YWCA. I had played a practical joke on the humourless manageress of the YWCA, whose name was Miss Bloxam. I had written to the Head Office of the Communist Party, in her name, and had said that she wished to join the Party. My action was discovered, only because I had boasted to all my friends about it, and Miss Bloxam had found me out. As a result, Bob had said I could stay at Headington Hill Hall for as long as I wanted to and Betty agreed with him.

Within about forty-five minutes, my father's car purred slowly down the drive, towards Headington Hill Hall. Mr Brightwell was driving.

"I'm going to hide from your scary driver," said Bob in jest. "I'll be hiding in one of the unoccupied offices!"

* * *

Bob wrote to me, at my London address, and asked me whether I would like to canvass for him in his North Bucks constituency, during the 1970 Election campaign. I replied to his letter and said I would.

Bob, Betty, Jean Baddeley, Judy Ennals, another secretary of Bob's, Bob's son, Philip, and I occupied a small but pleasant house overlooking a stagnant canal near the Labour Party Headquarters. These were in a town called Bletchley, later to become Milton Keynes. Jean knew I liked to take two baths a day, and organized a rigidly strict bath rota. She told me when I could take a bath, and added that my time in the bathroom should not exceed ten minutes. She only allowed me to take one bath a day and was known as "Bath Rota Baddeley."

Before the Election campaign had started, an anti-airport rally took place in a town somewhere in Buckinghamshire. The rally was organized by a Tory barrister called Desmond Fennell, who is now dead.

My parents invited him and his wife, Susan, to lunch in our Buckinghamshire house. Bob and Betty were also invited but she did not attend. The rally was due to take place later that afternoon.

My siblings, Nicky and Harriet, were also at the lunch, but my other brother, Adrian, was in America.

Bob had been put on yet another diet by Jean and Isabel, both of whom had lectured him about the importance of keeping to it rigidly. He refused to eat anything except soup. This was strange because he often insisted that he was not to be bullied by "a bunch of bloody hens".

Shortly after lunch, several cars set out for wherever the rally was due to take place. I chose to travel in the same car as Bob.

My mother had put heavy make-up onto my face, making me look like a tart. After most of the cars had left, Bob asked me to lead him upstairs to my mother's bathroom. He picked up a flannel, added soap and water to it and washed my face thoroughly. I told him that my mother had made up my face herself. I also told him, for some reason, that she had used Max Factor. "Max Factor is axel grease!" Bob commented assertively. I felt a curious thrill when he was washing my face.

Eventually, he took me to the Rolls Royce, which was driven by Mr Hoppitt once more.

I had already told Bob that I spoke fluent French and that I had taught myself Russian, because my parents would not allow me to have lessons. I think I mentioned this earlier in this book. I may have also mentioned that my mother wanted my third language to be Italian.

Mr Hoppitt lost his way. Bob hit him on the head with a rolled-up copy of *The Guardian*. Everyone was seated in the hall, where the anti-airport rally was due to take place.

My father was in the front row, with my mother, Nicky and my sister, Harriet. My parents were waiting anxiously for Bob and me.

I am sure my father suspected that impropriety had taken place between us. Although he (my father) was very lovable, he was rather old-fashioned and gave easily to suspicion, particularly about sexual matters.

He would never have believed me, if I had told him we were late because Bob had washed my face and his driver had lost the way.

During the journey, Bob and I spoke Russian. We were still speaking Russian when we walked down the aisle in the hall. Dumbfounded members of the public turned round and gaped at us. This delighted me because there is nothing I love more than an audience.

We both sat down in the row behind my family. Nicky found the whole thing "very amusing". Harriet raised her eyebrows in mischievous curiosity.

The rally had not yet started. Desmond Fennell had been waiting impatiently for Bob to arrive, before he started to make his speech.

"Hullo, Michael!" said Bob to my father, in a friendly tone of voice. "You've got a really smashing daughter!" Then he spoke Russian to me once more.

"Aren't you impressed by the way Eleanor's taught herself Russian?" he said to my father.

"I find it absolutely extraordinary," replied my father. "You haven't been teaching her, have you?"

"No, she did it all herself."

My father turned round and faced me. Bob was sitting next to me with one leg crossed over the other at right angles. It was a pose which suited him.

"How come you speak fluent Russian, when I have been paying for you to perfect your French? Come on, Eleanor Berry, come clean, out with it!" said my father.

"Eleanor already speaks perfect French. She doesn't need any more French lessons," said Bob.

My father was about to object, but Fennell banged the table for silence.

He was irritable by this time, and he didn't want his audience to be interrupted by the sound of Bob and me speaking Russian anymore.

After the rally, Bob promised to send me the complete Pergamon Press Russian course. This consisted of tapes and interesting stories, some of which were about incidents during the War. He kept his promise, as he always did. Two weeks' later, a crate, its contents worth about two hundred pounds, appeared on the doorstep of my parents' London house in Westminster.

We lived at 18 Cowley Street, from which it was possible to hear the soothing chimes of Big Ben at fifteen minute intervals. Harriet and I were living at 18 Cowley Street. My brothers had moved out.

It was at that time that there had been frequent printers' strikes on my father's two newspapers. The bastards had brought my father to his knees on countless occasions. Once, they had even brought the two papers to a standstill, by demanding two months' annual leave!

My mother became hysterical whenever there was a strike. She feared that we would go bankrupt. I was brought up to believe that I and my family would be begging in the streets, were the strikes to continue. I believed every word my mother uttered and began to save my pennies. I spoke with a thick Irish accent everywhere I went and I told all my friends I was poor. I never invited my friends to the house because I did not want them to know how we really lived.

* * *

Accompanied by the generous present was a nice, long letter from Bob. It took my mind off the dreadful printers' strikes. In his letter, Bob asked me if there was any way in which the course could be improved upon.

I wrote back to him in Russian. I asked my cousin, Laurence Kelly, a Russian speaker, a writer and a connoisseur of Russian history and literature, to lend me his Cyrillic typewriter. Laurence obliged.

I typed the letter with a considerable effort. It was a rather precocious letter, bordering on a love letter. It was about three hundred words long. I particularly remember the last paragraph in which I wrote, "Nothing fills me with greater pleasure and pride than the fact that I am your friend. I wish with all my heart, that we were sleeping in the same bedroom."

After I had posted the letter, I felt guilty, because of my devotion to Betty, whom I regarded as a surrogate mother. The act of betraying her was an anathema to me.

Part of me yearned to go to bed with her husband. Had he suggested I do so, I would have been incapable of refusing. I'm pleased he never asked me to, however. I would have felt bitterly ashamed afterwards, as if I had committed a murder.

It was my mother who once said to her friend, Dick Crossman, "Bob would never do such a thing to Eleanor. He is far too proper." (Crossman had cheekily asked her whether sexual relations had taken place between us.)

Bob didn't write back to me. I didn't expect him to do so. However, he told Nicky I had written to him, and asked Nicky whether he knew where I had managed to find a Cyrillic typewriter.

Nicky took me out to lunch in the City shortly afterwards. He said he knew about the letter and thought the whole thing was "damned amusing", one of his usual expressions.

"How did you manage to get hold of a Russian typewriter, old bean?" he asked. I told him I had borrowed Laurence's typewriter. I will never know, to this day, whether Bob had told Nicky about any material in the letter, and whether he had translated parts of it into English for my brother's benefit. I thought this would have been most unlikely, however, because Bob, God rest his soul, was a gentleman.

* * *

Once we had all moved into the Wharf House, at the start of the 1970 Election campaign, I thought Jean was being really impossible about her precious bath rota.

As I said earlier, at the time I needed two baths a day, because I was suffering from O.C.D., or Obsessive Compulsive Disorder. Indeed, I suffer from it today, although the attacks are far less severe. Jean thought I was most eccentric.

I had been trying desperately, if illogically, to wash away the catatonia, which the electro-convulsive therapy had caused me, Jean repeated that I would only be allowed one bath a day. I took my second bath in the house of a genial fellow called Mick, a factory foreman, who worked for the Labour Party. I'm afraid I can't remember his surname.

I've got a guilty confession to make. Very unwisely, and for reasons not even known to myself, I decided to dye my hair jet black. Perhaps, in my sub-conscious, I wanted to have the same coloured hair as Bob. I dyed my hair black in the factory foreman's bathroom and I inadvertently spilled black dye onto his towels.

I summoned the courage to tell him what I had done, and I offered to buy him new towels, but he was very agreeable and said it didn't matter.

Bob was far less understanding than the factory foreman. He was furious. He said black hair didn't suit me and he didn't mince his words either!

I took the train to London the following day, and returned to *Aldo Bruno's*, the Mayfair hairdresser's where I had repeatedly disgraced myself by reading *The Daily Worker*.

It took them two and a half hours to bleach my hair. I took the train to Milton Keynes and a taxi to Wharf House.

I told Bob I was sorry and he forgave me. He said how pretty I looked, now that my hair had been bleached. The bathing rota at the Wharf House was not the same as it had been at Headington Hill Hall. The bathroom, which was allocated to me in Headington, was at the top of the house, and I shared it with the luckless Jean

Baddeley. She constantly complained that I had taken all the hot water, and that I had left the bathroom stinking of Dettol. (At a much later date, Bob allowed me to use his and Betty's majestic bathroom, which was on the first floor, provided I refrained from using Dettol.)

There was only one bathroom in the Wharf House, as I said, but there were quite a few in Headington Hill Hall.

"Mr Maxwell has his bath at five o'clock in the morning," said Jean assertively, adding, "Woe betide you if you're in the bathroom at that time!" (She was referring to the bathroom at the Wharf House.)

I woke up, at quarter to three, feeling very hot and in need of a bath. I assumed no-one would be wanting to use the bathroom at three o'clock in the morning. Not so. Bob furiously banged on the door at three-thirty, while I lay, reading Edgar Allan Poe, in a piping bath, saturated with pine essence, on the other side of it.

"Philip (Bob's son), what the fucking hell are you doing in there!" shouted Bob angrily.

"It's not Philip. It's Eleanor," I said. As I spoke, I upset most of the bottle of pine essence onto *The Raven*.

"All right. I suppose I'll be able to come back in about three hours' time!" said Bob. He sounded like an out-of-work undertaker.

Philip, if I am right in saying so, appeared to be the black sheep of the Maxwell family, or at least in his father's eyes. There had apparently been a poor *rapport* between him and his father. Philip is rather a retiring man, and I believe he may have been scared of his father. Whenever his father intimidated or bullied him, he never fought back. Had he done so, the older man would have treated him better than he did and would have respected him.

He was the second of Bob's sons. His elder brother, Michael, a beautiful blond boy, had died following a fatal road accident. I have mentioned this before. Because the late Michael had been the first son, who could presumably have done no wrong, Philip must have had an inferiority complex about his new position as Bob's first son, and I think he felt very low in spirits about his alleged failure to match his late brother. Philip had psychiatric treatment for quite some time.

Betty rang me up in a really worried state, and begged me, due to my experiences with psychiatrists, to find Philip a "decent psychiatrist". (This was after Bob's death.)

I suggested a Harley Street doctor called Dr Peter Rohde, a hefty lefty and a fucking old woman. I will write more extensively about him later on in this book. I will not deny that Rohde was quite sympathetic.

In the end, Philip found a particularly nice man called Dr Robin Lawrence, who also practiced in Harley Street. (I know pretty well all the psychiatrists in this street.) I cannot think of a more kind-hearted or more accomplished psychiatrist than Dr Robin Lawrence.

I am told that Philip's inferiority complex and general negativity have much improved and that he is now working as a teacher somewhere in north London.

At the age of about eighteen, Philip went to South America and did not return to England for several years. I'm told he meant to get away from his father, whom he does not resemble in any way, although Bob must have been proud of him, after he had won a scholarship to Oxford.

When Philip went to South America, he joined forces with a woman called "Nilda". Bob sometimes called her "Dildo".

I really don't understand why Philip felt the need to go all the way to South America, simply to avoid a man who was living in Oxford! Why couldn't he have gone to London, or even Paris? I am sure Nilda would have agreed to accompany him, had he insisted on her doing so.

* * *

Jean's bath rota system simply wasn't working, at least not to my satisfaction. One morning, I used the bath at eight o'clock. I heard Betty's voice this time.

"Eléanore! Is that you in there again? Can you buck up?"

Betty needed to get into the bathroom, because the times stipulated on Jean's bath rota had overlapped, blast it!

I became very confused, so I begged Mick, the factory foreman to allow me to use his bathroom twice a day. From then on, I only used the bathroom in the Wharf House for cleaning my teeth and rinsing my mouth out.

Unfortunately, the factory foreman had become fed up with me, so I approached a widow called Cherry Goss, who also worked for Bob. I am afraid my reputation had spread throughout the entire North Bucks Labour Party and Mrs Goss turned my request down.

I found out that there was a public swimming pool, not too far from the Labour Party Headquarters. This meant I could go there whenever I wanted to immerse myself in water.

A man, aged about thirty, followed me from the swimming pool to the changing rooms. "If you strip off, I will give you a nice towelling down," he said vulgarly.

"I don't want either a nice towelling down, or a nasty towelling down," I replied, adding pompously, "I am not prepared to indulge in any form of sexual activity in Mr Maxwell's constituency."

I didn't go there again.

Finally, I used the public baths. This seemed to work out quite well. I didn't have any problems in the Wharf House after that.

* * *

There was no clocking-in system at the Labour Party Headquarters, so I wandered onto the premises, whenever I felt like it. The place I worked in was called the "Labour Hall". It was within the Labour Party Headquarters.

One of my duties was to wind the handle of a printing

press, which produced photocopies of Bob's photograph, as well as printed material about his policies. These were called "Maxwellgrams".

Sometimes, I sat at a rectangular table, accompanied by a few jolly, ribald old women, sitting in a row. We passed written material down a line. The person at the end of the line inserted the material into large envelopes, factory-style.

I was happy among these women. As we worked, we cracked filthy jokes. Bob came out of his office and into the Labour Hall, one day, while we sat working and joking. He reminded me of Rambo. He pushed our chairs, with us still sitting on them, to separate tables, scattered over the hall, and muttered something about lewd conversation giving the Labour Party a bad name.

Then he did the same thing to the chairs, occupied by about ten other workers, and pushed them, with the workers still sitting on them, to the table which he had taken us away from.

All this took him about five minutes. He had placed me next to a stranger. "I've put you next to a very good-looking man, so be sure to keep your conversation nice and clean," he said, adding, "Eleanor, this is Chris Brown."

"Forgive me, Bob," I said sweetly, giving him a seductive smile.

"I'll forgive you, but will the Almighty forgive you?" he replied.

Chris Brown was equally as saucy as the old women had been. Apart from having a pronounced lavatorial sense of humour, he liked to talk about the various disciplinary departments in the sex shops which he had visited in London.

"Bob said no lewd talk, Chris", I said piously.

"It's OK now. He's gone back to his office," Chris replied. He sounded like a ten-year-old-boy, accounting for the movements of his teacher.

I liked Chris. We often went out drinking together, once we had finished canvassing. He was lively and chatty, although sometimes, he was a bit moody. He was neither cultured not book-read, but he nearly always had a raunchy joke to crack, accompanied by an infectious laugh.

Occasionally, he took off my voice. I couldn't make up my mind about this. Sometimes, I found it amusing. Other times, I was irritated.

The Labour Party's canvassing van was an impressive sight, and was covered with painted slogans, such as, "Vote while you can. Maxwell's your man."

Mr Hoppitt was always behind the wheel, and Bob habitually stood up with his head and shoulders protruding through the roof, talking through a microphone.

"*Vote while you can. Maxwell's yer man,*" he boomed over and over again. He did this for about ten minutes at a time and finally asked Mr Hoppitt to pull into the side.

Mr Hoppitt swerved towards the pavement, on which a middle-aged woman was walking with her dog.

"Morning, madam," said Bob, in a friendly tone of voice. "That charming Basset of yours – what's his name?"

The woman appeared inappropriately hostile.

"He's not a Basset. He's a Border Terrier. If you really must know, his name's Jeff."

Bob looked piqued. He told Mr Hoppitt to move on.

* * *

I met another very nice man in the Labour Hall. He was older than some of the male canvassers. He was the Branch Secretary of some union or other and his name was Arthur Leary. He had a pleasant, gentle face, framed by thick, silvery hair, and spoke with a heavy Yorkshire accent. Sometimes, I worked at a table with him and Chris. We put stacks of envelopes into rubber bands and threw them into baskets.

If I wasn't having lunch at the Wharf House, Chris, Arthur,

Jean and I went to an Italian restaurant near the Labour Party Headquarters. Occasionally, Philip joined us.

At that time, I had a voracious appetite for food and I was never satisfied with what I had ordered. I drank a couple of gin and tonics, which made me hungrier still, and I leant over the table, holding my fork, with which I took things from Chris's, Arthur's and Jean's plates. I'm afraid I didn't have very good table manners at the time. Subconsciously, I had been imitating Bob's table manners.

Arthur was half amused and half irritated. He marched me into Bob's office after lunch. His Yorkshire accent was even more pronounced than usual.

"Your little girlfriend tairks things from oother people's plairts!" he complained. Bob looked disinterested.

"Don't worry about that, Arthur. I like her to take what she wants in life," he said.

I went canvassing that evening, accompanied by Betty and Ida, one of the women who had been cracking dirty jokes.

Ida was forthright and unusually talkative, like a washerwoman. Every time a bemused housewife answered her door, Ida launched into a manic monologue. She used inappropriately exaggerated language, and repeated, over and over again, how wonderful Bob was. She was doing more damage to the Labour Party than she thought she was doing.

I heard Betty's shrill French voice. She had been sitting in a second-hand banger which she invariably used for canvassing. Her other car was a Jaguar.

"Ida, come back to ze car and get in!" she shouted.

"Ida's not to canvass for me any more," said Bob to Betty at dinner.

"Who told you about Ida's canvassing?" Betty asked.

"Oh, just one of the other canvassers," said Bob, discreetly, "I'm not going to give names." (It was I who had grassed on Ida.)

Currently, I had been going from house to house with Betty.

"I want Eleanor to go out alone," said Bob at lunch one day. "I think it would give her more self-confidence and gain me a lot of votes."

I was happy at the prospect of going out alone, with my pile of canvassing sheets, leaflets and Maxwellgrams, some of which I had printed myself.

I started to work on a row of red brick houses with neatly-kept gardens.

"I'm canvassing on behalf of Robert Maxwell, the Labour candidate. Can we be counting on your vote on Polling Day?" I asked, on going to each house. Most of the houses were owned by Tories.

One of the housewives said, "Sorry, dear, I'm a rabid conservative," which made Bob laugh when I told him about it.

I got roughly the same reaction from the people behind the next few doors. I was getting bored, and I was tempted to record everyone in the street as being Tory, but I knew Bob wouldn't like me to do that, so I didn't.

I came to a house which was shabbier than the others. Also, the garden was overgrown. A man answered the door, wearing shirt sleeves and dark glasses. He looked like a gangster from the pages of Sapper.

"Fuck off, you common red tart!" he shouted. It was then that I made a heinous mistake, one which I am embarrassed about to this day.

I turned on my heels.

"Bob! A horrible man's just called me a 'common red tart'," I said, on going into his study.

Bob raised his head and looked at me through the whites of his eyes.

"Well, what did our Eleanor say to the man, then?" he asked.

"I ran away," I said, without thinking.

Bob continued to look at me through the whites of his eyes. He always did this when he was irritated.

"I won't have to do with people who run away, like frightened dogs, with their tails between their legs!" he said, his voice raised. "We Maxwells don't tolerate that sort of behaviour. We Maxwells are tough! I thought I'd tutored you well. Next time, you hit back. Do you understand?"

"Yes, Bob," I muttered.

"Just remember one thing, Eleanor. If you want something out of someone, you must learn how to terrify them out of their wits."

Later that evening, I went to the nearest pub with Chris and Arthur and we all got drunk. A few days later, I had an opportunity to meet with Bob's approval.

I was canvassing in a street in a really rough area. I was by myself. The inhabitants of most of the houses I approached, told me they would be voting Labour.

However, I knocked on a door which was opened by a bald-headed man in a dirty-looking, white boiler-suit. He was about thirty-five. There was a lot of rubbish in his hall, and the banisters on the facing staircase, looked as if they were about to fall off.

The man strode out of his house and came up to me. Our noses were almost touching.

"So, you're Labour, are you? It's because of this fucking Labour government that I've been out of work for five years. If you don't piss off, I'll give you a good backhander!" he shouted.

I was pleased because I knew I would have an opportunity to please Bob.

"Hit me then, you bastard, see if I care," I shouted back.

"You ain't fucking worth it," he replied.

He slammed the door in my face.

Jean had been canvassing in the same street. She had heard the man and me shouting at each other.

She was unable to hear the exact words of our heated exchange, but she looked impressed. "I wouldn't have dared to say half of what you were saying to that man," she said.

I was hoping that she would report the incident to Bob. I

thought this would impress him, more than my telling him myself.

Jean drove me back to the Wharf House in the second-hand banger. We went into Bob's study for a drink.

"You should have heard Eleanor just now. I thought that man was going to kill her. He and she were shouting their heads off," said Jean

"What man?" asked Bob.

"The man whose house she went to in XXX Street." His name has been recorded on the canvass sheet.

"Come on, *Basso Profundo*, let's have it. What happened?" Bob sometimes called me "*Basso Profundo*" because of my deep voice. He used the expression affectionately, whenever he liked my appearance and whenever I had done something to please him. Sometimes, he called me "Pussycat". Other times, he called me "Missy".

"Let's have it, *Basso Profundo*," he repeated. "What did you both say?"

I told Bob a few white lies because they were what he wanted to hear and would have enabled me to please him.

"I knocked on this man's door and told him I was canvassing for you," I began. "He asked me if I wanted him to give me a good shag up the arse. Sorry about the ribaldry, Bob. Then, I said, 'I doubt a freak like you would be able to get it up'!"

Bob let out his Coassak's laugh. I was fantastically turned on because I had managed to please him, even though I had told him a pack of lies. He smiled and asked me a rather bizarre question.

"Were you very depressed afterwards?"

"Depressed?"

"Depressed."

"No. Why should I have been depressed? I know I slipped up the last time, but there's nothing I like more than a good confrontation.[8*] I also marked the man's name and address on the canvass sheet, although it had been already."

[8*] It has always been my nature to be quarrelsome when I am provoked. This is due to my Smith blood (on my mother's side of the family). I am not a Smith for nothing.

Bob gave me a serious look and leant forwards in his chair.

"Good girl," he began, "Also, what you said to that man required a hell of a lot of courage. Do you know that?"

"Yes, maybe," I said, modestly. I felt as I imagined a heroin addict would feel after his first fix.

Even from childhood, I had had a phobia about being called a "coward." I longed to be told that I was courageous.

This was due to an occasion when I was eight. My oldest brother, Adrian, whom I had hero-worshipped, had walked me across some fields while thick snow covered the ground. We come to a very steep slope.

"I'm going to give you the best toboggan ride of your life, little sister," he said to me. "You're going to love it. Just hold onto me tight."

He pointed the toboggan down the steep slope. It went faster and faster. I was frightened and dug my heels into the snow, showing us down.

"You've spoilt our ride," he said furiously. "Go home! I don't play games with cowards."

Due to my hero worship of him, I felt mortified.

I worked hard for the following few days, and enjoyed the company of my favourite workers, Chris Brown and Arthur Leary. We continued to go out canvassing in the evenings.

Chris and I were canvassing on opposite sides of a street in Newport Pagnell, a sedate, xenophobic village. I walked up a tall flight of steps, my hands full of leaflets and Maxwellgrams. I knocked on one of the doors. It was answered by an exceptionally thin, old woman with beady eyes.

"I'm canvassing on behalf of Robert Maxwell, the Labour candidate. Can we be counting on your vote next Thursday?" I began.

The old woman stared at me. I stared back at her, until she averted her gaze. Suddenly, she formed her wizened hands into fists and pummelled me violently on the top of my arms.

"Take your stinking literature off my threshold!" she shouted at the top of her voice. Her accent wasn't local. She could have been a colonial. Also, her choice of words was dated.

She seized some of my papers and screwed them into balls, which she threw down the steps into the street. I wondered what she was going to do next and I didn't wait in vain. She continued to pummel me on the arms, with both hands, but as she was doing so, she freed one of her arms and gave a Nazi salute.

When her arm was tired, she sang the National Anthem. I waited for her to finish and struggled to keep a straight face.

"You're absolutely bonkers!" I said. "Do you realize that?"

The next thing I knew was that the fruitcake had pushed me down her steps. I had still been able to hold onto some of the canvass sheets, as well as a few Maxwellgrams.

Chris came over to me and helped me to my feet. With a trembling hand, I wrote the words, "VERY DANGEROUS WOMAN" against her name on the canvass sheet.

Chris looked at the canvass sheet and let out a guffaw. I had hurt my arm slightly when falling. Chris drove me back to the Wharf House.

Bob was in the kitchen. He wasn't wearing a jacket. The top two buttons of his shirt were undone and his tie was loosened at the neck. His appearance set my blood on fire, as it invariably did when he loosened his tie at the neck. I am always turned on by men who do this. I don't know why.

Chris had already told Jean roughly what had happened. Jean was in Bob's study, making a phone call.

"Eleanor was attacked this evening, Bob" said Chris, "she hurt her arm."

"Attacked? Blimey!" shouted Bob. He added, "Come into the kitchen everyone, and have some scrambled eggs." (Several campaign workers were in the house as well.)

Bob, oddly enough, was a good cook. He had cooked the scrambled eggs with butter, as opposed to milk and they tasted much better than they would have tasted, had they been cooked with milk.

"What exactly happened, Eleanor?" he asked, as he doled out the scrambled eggs from the saucepan and put them onto plates.

He gave me the audience I craved, which made me forget about the mild pain in my arm. I was supremely happy once more.

"So, this barmy old woman started to hit you?" he said.

"Yes. That's right. Let me show you what she did." Bob sat down.

I did the same to Rob as the woman had done to me. When I was hitting his arms, I realized how cuddly he was. He threw back his head and laughed.

"Steady, Missy, you're beating me up!" he said.

I did a demonstration of the woman singing the National Anthem, and of her giving a Nazi salute with one arm, while continuing to hit me with the other.

"You hurt your arm when she pushed you down her steps, didn't you?" he said.

"Yes."

Bob put two fingers of each hand into his mouth and wolf-whistled. Jean came into the kitchen.

"I do wish you'd stop that awful whistling, every time you want to attract my attention, Mr Maxwell," she said. "It really is awfully common."

"It's what they do at football grounds, isn't it?"

"What can I do for you, Mr Maxwell?" asked Jean coldly.

"Get a doctor. I think she may have hurt her arm."

"It's OK. I don't need a doctor," I said. Once more, I made the mistake of looking Bob in the eye. I began to feel faint, due to his attractive appearance and glittering hazel eyes.

Betty suddenly came into the kitchen and kissed her husband on the forehead.

I stood up and motioned her to my chair. I could feel the

blood draining away from my face. I held onto the back of the chair with both hands.

"You're looking very pale, Eléanore. Are you not feeling well?" asked Betty, in a sympathetic tone of voice.

"I... I... er I am all right, thank you. There's no need for you to worry about me," I eventually managed to mutter.

I left the kitchen and went into Bob's study. I sat down on an upright chair and put my head between my knees. Somehow, this prevented me from fainting.

* * *

I went canvassing with Chris Brown the following evening.

I had knocked on a door, which was opened by an unshaven drunk. The man supported himself precariously on the half-open door and stared at me with watery red eyes, exhaling the stench of stale whisky.

I said my spiel.

"I don't vote for crooks," he said.

"Your words are slanderous and I will write them down. I know your name," I replied.

He tried to slam the door in my face but I jammed it open with my foot.

"What you really resent about Mr Maxwell is the fact that he started with less than you and got further. You're a petty-minded, provincial lout!" I shouted.

The man swayed backwards and forwards, as if he were about to fall over. Chris came to my side.

"Leave him!" he commanded. "Just mark on the canvass sheet that he's not voting Labour. There's no time to turn up at people's houses and make long speeches, even if they are in Bob's favour. He added, "If you want to say something flattering about him, keep it brief". He then quoted an old-fashioned saying, "*Here Endeth the First Lesson*".

The following day, Bob called me into his study. I was terrified, because I thought he was going to break sad news about the death or an illness of someone in my family.

"Has someone been taken ill?" I asked urgently.

Bob was looking as serious as a High Court Judge. I continued to fear the onset of bad news. "Has someone been taken ill?" I repeated.

Bob came to the point without preamble.

"Eleanor! You are *not* to frighten my constituents!"

"But you taught me to do so, Bob," I protested.

Bob cleared his throat loudly. He sounded like a gang of Hell's Angels trying to start their motorbikes.

"I understand that, but don't do it in *my* bloody constituency. I'm trying to win this election, for Christ's sake!"

"I promise not to do this in your constituency, ever again, Bob," I said.

"It's all right, Pussycat. I know your heart's in the right place. Tomorrow, just to make sure things are all right, I'll get Philip to go round with you."

Philip, although rather unhappy for some of the time, is humorous, gentle and very amusing. He doesn't appear to have inherited any of his father's genes, as I have pointed out before.

As Philip and I got out of the banger to canvass in one of the streets, he said, "Whatever you do, don't be rude to anyone, Ellie. You may come across some ghastly old fart, but be sure to be as polite as possible."

"No problem, Philip," I replied. "Your father gave me a talking to last night."

"I can well imagine he did! He sometimes tends to be the pot that calls the kettle black, if you'll pardon the cliché. He can be brutal sometimes but he's got a kind heart and I try to get on with him."

I didn't know whether Philip really meant what he had said. After all, he had once run away to South America in order to get away from his father. Part of him must have hated his father.

* * *

Betty and I sometimes canvassed together. Strangely, we shared an interest in the Marquis de Sade, the self-confessed flagellomaniac. I like to refer to him as "de Soggins".

I couldn't understand why Betty had been so upset on a much later occasion, when Ghislaine had phoned her from New York and had spoken to her about the "canings". (I have accounted for this incident earlier in the book.) At an earlier period of her life, however, Betty, had expressed a great interest in the master of flagellation, namely the Marquis de Sade.

Once during the campaign, Betty and I took a break from canvassing. We sat down on a seat in a village street and drank coffee from a flask.

A passionate, but friendly argument took place between us, about whether the 1787 edition of the Marquis de Sade's novel, *Justine* had more or fewer merits than the altered 1797 edition.

Betty said she thought the 1787 edition had more merits, because of its recurrent theme that virtue is always rewarded, whereas vice is punished in the end.

I did not adhere to her view, however. I said, tactfully, that I believed that an act of virtue seldom achieves very much, not even a minor reward or an acknowledgement. I referred to the innocent victims of the Holocaust and the way in which they had been tortured and murdered.

Later on in the conversation, Betty told me she was doing an MA in Philosophy and French literature. She referred to one of the Marquis de Sade's views, namely that in every pleasure there was pain. I wondered whether she had been referring to the sex act, but I thought it would have been more than inappropriate to ask her, although I was tempted to do so.

I gave a lot of thought to Ghislaine's phone call in later years, and remembered how upset she (Betty) had been when I had woken up that day. I concluded that her attitude towards flagellation had changed substantially over the years. Either that, or she didn't care for it on her own doorstep.

Chris Brown called to us. He was leaning out of the campaign van, which, as always, was driven by Mr Hoppitt, who had just pulled in.

"It's past lunch time," said Chris, "Lunch is at one o'clock, and it's now one thirty. Are you OK, both of you?"

"Yes, perfectly," answered Betty. "Eléanore and I have been arguing about a Frenchman."

She and I got into the campaign van and continued our argument, about the 1787 edition of *Justine*, as opposed to the 1797 edition. Both Chris and Mr Hoppitt were baffled.

"I've got a set of the Marquis de Sade's works at Headington Hill Hall," said Betty. "Would you like to borrow them once this Election campaign is over?"

"Yes, I'd like that very much. You *are* kind!"

"They're bound in pink satin. When you've finished with them, could you please return them to me? I don't normally lend satin-bound books to anyone, particularly if they belong to a set. You will look after them, won't you?"

"Yes, of course I will."

I thanked her. After the election was over and we were back at Headington Hill Hall, she put the books into a plastic bag, which she handed to me. The books were all explicitly illustrated and were in French.

It gives me a headache to read French as I have said earlier. However, I took some Paracetamol and bit the bullet and decided to read one of the books in French.

Although I shouldn't have done so, I took the books to my parents' villa in the South of France, so that I could read them on holiday. The villa was called "Villa Carmel". My father had designed it and had had it built in 1969.

The first book by de Soggins, which I began to read, was *Les 120 journées de Sodome* (*120 days of Sodomy*). It is by far his most obscene book. It also has some pretty naughty illustrations in it.

I used a bookmark and read sections from *Les 120 journées de Sodome*, which I kept on my bedside table.

I left the book there during the day, assuming that it was safe to do so.

My mother was a proverbial nosy-parker, however. She found the book on my bedside table, together with all the other novels by de Soggins, which I had kept in my suitcase, in the plastic bag that Betty had given me.

My mother looked briefly at the illustrations in *Les 120 journées de Sodome,* as well as those in the other books. She confiscated them all.

"I'm taking all these books away," she said. "Some of them are very nasty."

"You can't do that! They all belong to Mrs Maxwell. They're part of a beautifully bound set," I protested.

"You are talking absolute crap!" my mother retorted. "I'm afraid I can't allow such obscene books in my house."

"Then I'll ring up Mrs Maxwell and I'll tell her you've stolen her books. Then she'll sue you." I said, adding, "If she doesn't sue you, her husband will and he's never lost a case in his life!"

"There's no need to be rude," said my mother.

However, she had already seized the bag of books and had slammed the door behind her.

I didn't know what to do. Eventually, I bribed my mother's butler, with five hundred francs, the equivalent of fifty pounds, and I asked him to look for the books. He knew all my mother's hiding places.

He found them in a cupboard in her bathroom. (My parents had separate bathrooms.) I took them from him, handed him the five hundred francs, wrapped them up in a bath towel and walked over to the clothes line, where I started to collect my washing.

My mother found me there. She must have had eyes in the back of her head. I continued to keep the books hidden in the bath towel.

"I'm sorry you went so far as to bribe my butler, to find those horrible books," said my mother mildly.

"They're *not* my books. They belong to Mrs Maxwell. I've told you this before." I continued, "Would you like me to ring Mrs Maxwell up, so that you can speak to her? The books are all bound in pink satin, as you can see, and altogether, they must be worth hundreds of pounds."

It was then that my father suddenly came onto the scene. He was wearing his formal London suit and was looking gutted.

"I've got bad news for you, Pam," he said, adding, "I've got to take the next plane back to London.

"It's the printers, I'm afraid. They're asking for two months' holiday a year, yet again. Unless I do something about it now, *The Daily Telegraph* and *The Sunday Telegraph* will die."

"Oh my God!" exclaimed my mother. "It's not as if you yourself took two months' holiday a year. You work like a bloody pit pony. God, they're bastards!"

I continued to keep the books hidden in the towel. I felt intensely sorry for my father. The printers had done this sort of thing on countless occasions in the past, and their persistent blackmailing had never failed to make my father ill, and had caused by mother, who was of a somewhat hysterical disposition, to be worried sick.

When we were living at 18 Cowley Street, the conversation at the dinner table had almost always been about printers' strikes and the damage they were doing to my father's trade. My mother, who was highly-strung and pessimistic, constantly told me that the family business was at risk of folding and that we would all become destitute as I said before. She must have inherited her fear of poverty from her father, F. E. Smith. He always insisted that he had risen from intense poverty to riches.

According to a biography of F. E. Smith, by his son, Freddie Birkenhead, my maternal uncle, F. E. Smith had never been poor, even during his childhood. Indeed, his family had always been comfortably off.

"F. E. Smith", to quote the words of his son, "was fond of emphasizing in later years that he had made his way in life largely unaided. When he was created a peer in 1919, he inscribed upon his crest the defiant caption, *"Faber meae Fotunae"* – "Smith of my own fortune".

Bob, on the other hand, though similar to F. E. Smith in many ways, particularly where his personality was concerned, had originated from the most horrendous poverty.

I phoned Nicky in horror and asked him whether my mother's fears of our family being reduced to abject poverty, were justified.

"Don't pay any attention to that kind of talk, old bean," he said reassuringly.

"I can't bear living with Mummy and Daddy, because all they talk about are printers' strikes, bankruptcy and destitution," I said, adding, "Mummy says our family will be reduced to begging in the streets."

"Absolute balderdash!" said Nicky.

"I can't bear living at 18 Cowley Street any more."

"Pack your bags and move in with me, old bean."

Nicky and I lived together, in a house in Kensington, known as Rutland Gate. We lived there on and off for some time My room overlooked a leafy park. I was happy when I was living with Nicky. The wonderful thing about him was that he always saw a funny side to all things grave. Also, he never tried to get into my head. There was another good thing about him: he hated displays of emotion. I know I've mentioned all this before.

I rarely display emotion, except anger. The display of emotion is distasteful to me.

I learned to type and to take shorthand. I took temporary

jobs all over London. When it was time for me to do my A' Levels in English, French and Russian, I left Rutland Gate for a while and studied at a college in Oxford, called the Oxford College of Further Education. This meant I could be close to the Maxwells. I lived in the Y.W.C.A. at first, but only for a short period of time.

As I explained earlier, the woman who ran the Y.W.C.A., threw me out. I have already told the reader *why* she threw me out, so I won't repeat myself. What I will emphasize, however, is the fact that the Maxwells very kindly allowed me to stay in their house for a year and for longer, if necessary, rent-free.

* * *

To get back to my holiday at the Villa Carmel, my mother, my eldest brother, Adrian, his wife, Marina and I, stayed in the villa for a few more days, before returning to London. I secreted all Betty's books, contained in the plastic bag, in my suitcase.

I stayed with my parents at 18 Cowley Street, for two nights. Then I planned to stay with the Maxwells. I had a throat infection, so I visited the seductive Dr Goldman, who gave me a prescription for some antibiotics. My appointment with him was not until five thirty p.m., by which time most of the chemists were closed. Also, it was a Friday.

I had dinner alone, in a steak house in Victoria Street and took a taxi to an all-night chemist in Kilburn. The man behind the prescriptions counter, told me that he had the antibiotics I needed, but that he wouldn't be able to give them to me for at least half an hour.

This irritated me because I didn't know the area. I walked about for a good fifteen minutes, until I came to a wild-sounding pub called "*Biddy Mulligan's*". I needed a drink, so I went in. The place was exceptionally crowded.

I waited my turn and ordered a double gin and tonic. I was very pleased by the fact that I had brought Betty's copy of "*Les*

120 Journées de Sodome" in my handbag, and that I would probably be able to finish it. I sat down in a corner, drank a little and started to read.

When I looked up, I saw a man shaking a tin on which there was a label on the tin saying, "HELP THE PERSECUTED CATHOLICS IN ULSTER".

The man shook the tin and started chanting, "Hey hey hey, for the IRA."

It was only then that I realized I was in an IRA pub. However, most of the gin had gone to my stomach and had helped me to relax.

I continued to read and I couldn't help being rather shocked by a passage, which I certainly don't intend to translate into English. The passage referred to: "*un vieux homme de quatre-vingt-dix ans, avec un petit garçon de six ans, chacun en train de chier dans la bouche de l'autre, et après avoir chié, ils ont avalé la merde, et ensuite, ils ont vomi d'une force ravisante.*"

I drank some more gin. A man, aged about forty, came over and sat in the chair next to mine. He blew the stench of stale beer into my face. His mouth was touching my ear. To my horror, he started to talk to me.

"This man, the Marquiss de Sayeed, did he ever do any good for Ireland?" he asked. His speech was slurred and he had a heavy Belfast accent. I drank more gin and tonic, before I answered his question. I knew I couldn't afford to speak to him with an English accent, so I effected a bogus French accent.

"I'm afraid he spent most of his life in prison, but if he had not been in prison, I'm sure he would have buckled down and done his bit for the place," I replied.

My answer satisfied the man, who introduced himself as "Sean". He bought me another double gin and tonic, which I drained. I excused myself and said I wasn't feeling very well. I hurriedly left the IRA pub, and found my way back to the chemist, where I collected my antibiotics.

The following day was a Saturday. I still hadn't passed my driving test, so I took the train to Oxford and a taxi to Headington Hill Hall.

"Let's hear about your adventures, Missy," said Bob, who was sitting in the drawing room, just before lunch. Betty was sitting near him on the Empire sofa.

I told the Maxwells that my mother had confiscated all Betty's books, but that I had bribed her butler to show me where she had put them. I added that I had hidden them by wrapping them up in a bath towel.

I then said that there had been another printers' strike on *The Daily Telegraph*, which had caused my mother to forget about the books. I refrained from telling the Maxwells about my visit to the IRA pub, as I thought that Bob wouldn't have approved. I also knew that Betty would have been cross, had she found out that I had taken one of her intricately bound books into a pub.

I assured Betty that all her books were intact and that I would bring them downstairs after lunch. I added that I had nearly finished *"Les 120 Journées de Sodome"*. She laughed, "That's the naughtiest of all Sade's works!" she remarked.

Bob gave one of his wolf-whistles. Oping came into the drawing-room and said that lunch was ready.

Bob took me aside, as we were going into the diningroom. "How much money did you give to the butler when you bribed him?" he asked.

"Five hundred francs," I replied.

He gave the guttural Cossack's laugh characteristic of him.

"Good!" he said.

Ghislaine and Jean were the only people in the dining-room, apart from Bob, Betty and myself. Bob kept taking Ghislaine on his knee, cuddling her and smothering her with kisses. She was an adult by this time. I can't emphasize enough how jealous I was of her. What made me particularly jealous was the fact that her father had frequently beaten her when she was younger.

* * *

Let's get back to Bob's Election campaign in June 1970, quite some time before all these events occurred.

I was in an idyllic square with Chris and Arthur, in the centre of a village, called Newport Pagnell. We were standing among a crowd. The scenario could have belonged to eighteenth century Italy.

Creepers hung in abundance from the walls of a pub, outside which sat three overweight, cloth-capped rustics, with their backs to the crowd. Their braces were so tight that they looked as if they were about to snap. They were swigging from big, brimming beakers of beer and stuffing themselves with fish and chips, which they had bought in a shop next door to the pub.

They were eating and drinking so greedily, that they failed to speak to each other, although they appeared to know each other. I looked at them and formed the opinion that they were unpleasant.

Bob's campaign van (driven by Mr Hoppitt, as ever) pulled up in front of the crowd. The date was 10th of June, 1970, Bob's birthday. Many of his supporters sang "Happy Birthday" which appeared to irritate and embarrass him.

He leant out of the roof of the van and addressed his audience, speaking as usual, about unions, the allegedly unhygienic lavatories at Eton, corrupt landlords persecuting their tenants, tied cottages and subjects of that ilk.

I noticed the three rustics, even more bloated with beer, getting up from their seats and staggering towards the van.

I picked up a heavy stick and walked towards them.

Bob tried to crack a joke.

"It's lucky there's a shop selling fish and chips so close to the pub, isn't it?" he said.

"You wouldn't be standing up there like that, if you'd been able to buy *The News of the World*!" shouted one of the rustics.

77

"I don't think this is an occasion to be personal," replied Bob mildly.

The rustic moved even closer. I got as close to him as I could. I was clutching the stick, my heart awash with hatred and carnal pleasure at the same time.

"How can you call yourself a socialist, if you own a Rolls-Royce and have trusts for your children in Liechtenstein?" the rustic asked.

Bob lost his temper.

"Your remarks are slanderous. You are deliberately instigating a smear campaign against me! I'll take your name!"[9*] he shouted.

I raised the stick and held it behind me. I was about to bring it down on the back of the rustic's head with full force. I felt another surge of eroticism.

"Eleanor! Naughty!" shouted Bob. I was so startled that I took three paces backwards, and slowly opened my hand to release the stick which fell to the ground. The incident could have easily been filmed in slow motion.

* * *

It was found out towards the end of the campaign, that Bob's agent, a militant Left-winger called Jim Lyons, bore a grievance against his boss. Lyons had failed to complete the administrative work required of him, and had been bullying his pro-Maxwell deputy agent, Bill Turner.

This wretched man was devoted to Bob, but he was too weak and cowardly to stand up to Lyons.

Turner suffered from a mental illness, brought on by Lyons's idleness, devious conduct in general and pathological hatred of Bob. Lyons was also known to be extremely anti-Semitic.

[9*] It wasn't until some years had passed, that I found out the rustic's name: It was Oliver Smedley and he lived in Newport Pagnell. It was Nicky who gave me this information. God knows how he obtained it!

Turner had repeatedly tried to tell Bob about Lyons's behaviour and had referred, incoherently, to his mental state. His methods of expressing himself were muddled, confused and, for want of a better word, incomprehensible. As a result, Bob became impatient whenever Turner approached him, as he only liked people who were concise.

On one occasion, Lyons had been driving the campaign van, without Bob's permission. The van had run out of petrol in a village street, most of whose inhabitants were Labour voters.

The loudspeakers was turned on and Lyons started to swear his head off. Four letter words blasted, not only round the Labour Party headquarters, but also to the ears of the inhabitants of the village street, many of whom probably decided to vote Conservative as a last resort. Lyons completely lost it and shouted about his demented hatred of his boss.

Arthur Leary took command of the situation brilliantly, and rushed over to the nearest microphone in the Labour Party Headquarters.

"Watch the language you're using! You're on hot mike," he shouted.

"I'll use what fucking language I choose to use," replied Lyons. "I'm out of bloody fuel."

"I'll tell Mr Maxwell," said Arthur.

"Tell anyone you fucking well like! You know what I think of that bastard."

Bob came into the room, while Lyons's tirade was continuing.

"Where the hell's Lyons?" he demanded.

"He's taken the campaign van and he's out of fuel," said Arthur mildly. "Also, he's abusing the microphone."

"He's taken the van, without asking me? Where the hell's Turner?"

"I'm afraid Bill Turner has gone to see his psychiatrist, Bob," said Arthur.

"Why?"

"Because Jim Lyons has been bullying him to such an extent that he's gone off his head. Also, Lyons hates your guts," replied Arthur.

"Why the hell didn't Turner come to see me about Lyons?" asked Bob.

"He *did* come to see you, but you weren't able to understand a word he said."

"In that case, I don't think his psychiatrist will either," said Bob.

Arthur hinted that Lyons had been bone-idle throughout the campaign.

"Why the fucking hell didn't you tell me that Lyons was bringing Turner to his knees!" shouted Bob, adding, in a gloomy tone of voice, "I'm not too confident we're going to win this bloody Election, Arthur."

* * *

Bob was doing his "surgery" the following day. An agitated woman brought her daughter, a waif-like creature, aged about fourteen, into his office. The mother of the fourteen-year-old girl told Bob that her daughter was pregnant, and asked him what she should do about it.

Bob addressed all his questions to the girl, rather than her mother. Throughout the first part of the interview, he was pleasant and sympathetic.

"Why can't you marry the baby's father, when you come of age, settle down and make a go of it?" he asked.

"I couldn't possibly do that," said the girl hysterically.

"Why not?"

"Because I don't know who the father is, Mr Maxwell."

"Why the hell don't you know who the flaming father is?" asked Bob, his voice raised.

"Well, it could be one of five, Mr Maxwell. It could be Eric, John, Martin, Burt or Bruce."

"What do you mean?" demanded Bob.

"It's simple, Mr Maxwell," said the girl, "It was a bloody Saturday night and I had a gang bang, didn't I?"

Bob looked at the girl aghast.

"Blimey, Miss, you really have put my King in check!" was all he could think of saying.

This anecdote travelled all over the constituency, almost at the speed of light. It was told, with increasing exaggeration in pubs, cafés, restaurants and many other places. It also got into the local papers. The story was favourable to Bob because of its humorous and responsible nature. It gained him a large number of votes, even though it didn't win him his seat outright. It was the infamous Jim Lyons who caused him to lose.

* * *

Ida, the very noisy woman, whom I wrote about earlier, was frequently accompanied by her elderly mother, who also made a lot of noise. The two women were often together in the Labour Hall, doing administrative work for Bob.

Ida's elderly mother started to bring her father onto the premises. He looked about a hundred and three. He was brought in, because there was nobody to look after him at home.

He occupied a chair at the back of the Labour Hall. His head, which was covered with snow-white hair, was invariably thrown back, his eyes were closed and his toothless mouth gaped open.

Those, who saw him for the first time, assumed that he was dead, and a few women screamed on seeing him.

Sometimes, Bob resurrected the situation by walking past him, ruffling his hair, patting him on the back and muttering, "How yer doin', Grandpa?"

Betty was terrified of the man.

"Do we *have* to have him in here, Bob? He gives me the creeps. 'Is he dead?' I keep asking myself."

"No, of course he isn't dead! He's got nowhere else to go. He's staying here," replied Bob.

"But, Papa" (she often called him this), "He seems to be in perpetual rigour. He makes the place look like a mortuary."

"I've told you already, he's staying, so stop talking about it!"

"Is there any reason why he can't sit in your office?" asked Betty.

"I don't want him in my blasted, bloody office!" shouted Bob.

Many of the campaign workers assumed that the old man was more likely to be dead than alive, but he became accepted as part of the furniture.

* * *

The Tory candidate, a drab, colourless, middle-aged man called Bill Benyon made his speech on the Eve of Polls, much earlier than Bob', who said Benyon needed to be heckled. Isabel and I took up our positions in the audience. Isabel shouted that things would get even worse if the Tories got in. She added, "What about the children who would be having a two-tier education under the Tories?"

Several Tories interrupted her. I couldn't hear what any of them were saying.

I got up and made a speech, addressing Benyon. I referred bitingly to a number of issues, although I can't remember, for the life of me, what these were. I had taken a notebook with me. I can't speak properly without notes, but once I have notes, I am a reasonable speaker.

Isabel drove me back to the Wharf House in the yellow Morris Minor, which she shared with her twin sister, Christine. We went into Bob's study. I did all the talking: "Isabel said (whatever she had said) and I said I had shouted Benyon into a silence." I quoted Bob whatever words I had used.

"Good!" said Bob kindly. "I don't think even I would have been able to think of those things spontaneously."

*** *** ***

Bob made a passionate Eve of Polls speech at the Labour Hall. Cameras clicked and flashed around him. Occasionally, his audience cheered. I experienced the same thrill as I had had, when Bob had washed my face that day. However, it became apparent, due to a smell, similar to that of rotten meat, that the old man at the back had indeed died. In fact, his body had been decomposing.

Even Bob, with his repeated hair-ruffling and "How yer doin', Grandpa?" had no knowledge that he had been touching up a stiff.

A certain amount of bustling took place around the chair in which the old man had been sitting.

Bob's speech was over, and was followed by tumultuous applause and the further flashing of cameras. Many of his supporters had risen to their feet, preparing to leave the Labour Hall to cast their votes.

A short man, wearing a dog collar, mounted the platform and gave Bob a note. He read it and looked startled.

"I think one ought to generally send for an ambulance," he said, in the tone of a man asking his barber for a short back and sides.

"A bloomin' ambulance should 'ave come 'ten friggin' days ago!" shouted a male Labour Party supporter. He seemed a bit the worse for wear.

The campaign workers crowded into Bob's study in the Wharf House. Most of us sat on the floor. Some women chatted, in high-pitched voices about the old man's death. Others were laughing nervously. I couldn't hold out any longer. The whole situation had turned into a macabre farce. I was absolutely convulsed with giggles, due to my love of black comedy. I tried to give the impression I was crying.

"What's the matter, Eléanore?" asked Betty.

"It's all right. I think I'll go outside for some fresh air," I said.

I staggered outside and waited for my laughing attack to subside, before going back to the house. When I went indoors, I saw Bob in the hall.

I kissed him on the cheek and wished him good luck.

"I may well need it, Eleanor. A lot of people round here think I'm a bloody Bolshevik!" he said.

Everyone was waiting for the first results to come through on the television. I sat on the floor once more, near Bob's feet. Attention had turned rapidly from stiffs to polls. The first results had not yet come through, though.

I felt guilty, once more, because I had taken the train to London, where I had voted Conservative. During later Elections, I did exactly the same thing. Once I had gained a driving licence, I drove Labour Party supporters to the polls, using my late brother, Adrian's car. He was furious.

I felt so disturbed, when I was driving Labour Party supporters to the polls, that I took 60mg of Diazepam, or Valium, half an hour before I got into the car. Doctors say 60mg is a colossal dose but I have always been able to tolerate it.

The drug calmed me and I became quite elated. I sang a barrack room ballad, and most of the fuckers in the back of the car really enjoyed it. Some old ladies were sitting on the knees of other old ladies.

"It's the same, the whole world over,
It's the poor what gets the blame,
And the rich what gets the pleasure.
Ain't it all a bloomin' shame?"

My puzzled passengers sang the barrack room ballard with me, on their way to the polls. Although I am a Tory, and a Tory voter, I wanted Labour to win in Bob's constituency.

* * *

It was on the cards, due to the opinion polls, that Labour would win on a landslide in the summer Election of 1970.

I continued to sit on the floor, at Bob's feet, near Chris, Jean and Arthur. Bob sat behind his desk with the top two buttons of his shirt undone and his tie loosened, which, as always, drove me into a frenzy.

The results began to come through. After about an hour, it transpired that Labour was losing, contrary to what the opinion polls had predicted. Most of Bob's family, including Betty, looked downcast. Some of the female campaign workers were in tears.

When Bob's close friend, the controversial, hard-drinking George Brown, lost his seat, him was sorry for him. I once asked Bob what he thought of George Brown.

"He's a very good friend of mine," replied Bob. "He has his faults but don't we all?"

I was greatly ennobled by his remark, because I am sometimes unable to forgive my friends' faults.

There was a hush in the room. The silence was broken by a disastrously tactless remark, made by Ian, one of Bob's sons. He is my favourite of all the Maxwell children. He was then aged about fourteen. He was addressing his elder sister, Isabel.

Ian is, and always has been, a delightful person. He fills rooms with life and laughter, wherever he goes. However, there may well have been occasions during his early life, when he had offered the putter to a player whose golf ball was still in a bunker. He has never harmed anyone, intentionally or otherwise, although, when he got carried away, he had in the past, been a trifle thoughtless, without meaning to be.

"What do you think, Izzy?" he asked, his voice raised above the sound of the television, "When it comes to Dad's constituency, there'll be a couple of recounts before he finally loses. His remark was indeed undiplomatic. I can only attribute it to the possibility of his having consumed a few drinks beforehand.

I don't know or not whether Ian found his father formidable. He has always professed to loving him, when he was younger, or indeed when he reached adulthood, and whenever his father reprimanded him, he invariably answered back.

Perhaps, on that one isolated occasion, Ian may have found Bob's study claustrophobic, due to its small size and also the amount of people occupying it on Election night. It was not unlike an underground train during the rush hour.

Although Ian may possbily have had a drink or two, he may have been severely sensitive to the heat, which could have irritated him and caused him to make the tactless remark. There was no air-conditioning in Bob's office and the heat was overbearing.

Isabel didn't answer her brother and lowered her head. Bob looked away from the television and focused his angry eyes on his son.

"I'd watch it, if I were you, or you'll be sorry," he said, adding, "That means I'll give you a bloody good hiding!"

The rebuke made me feel very excited but I stayed where I was, on the floor. I looked briefly at some of Bob's supporters. They all looked disappointed.

The craggy face of Reginald Bosanquet filled the screen. He has never struck me as being particularly good-looking.

Anne, Bob's elder daughter, whom I had already met, had just taken her Finals. She evidently fancied Bosanquet, and tried to cheer the gloomy atmosphere in the room. She mimicked a Cockney accent.

"'Ullo, dearie! Fancy a roll in the 'ay, dearie? Don't squeeze the fruit, if you ain't goin' to buy it!"

"Shut up, Anne!" shouted Bob. "I can't hear a bloody thing when you're cracking stupid jokes. One more sound out of you, and I'll take you upstairs and tan your backside!"

The two threats of the infliction of corporal punishment, by the hand of the ravishing male sex siren, were more than I could handle. The lust they inspired in me, caused me to hyperventilate. I went upstairs and immersed myself in a cold bath for half and hour.

I returned to Bob's study, assuming that my absence had not been noticed.

"Where the hell have you been, Eleanor?" asked Bob, his tone of voice half amused and half angry. "Surely, you couldn't have had yet another bath. Jean said you had two already today."

"I was answering a call of nature," I lied.

* * *

We stayed up until about four o'clock in the morning, by which time we knew that the Tories were winning.

The count in Bob's constituency would not be taking place until later on in the morning.

The campaign workers, including Chris and Arthur, began to shuffle despondently out of Bob's study. I got up. My legs were very stiff and it took me a long time to stand up straight.

Bob stroked my cheek.

"Thank you so much, Eleanor," he said.

"For what? I've failed. We all have," I replied in a gloomy tone of voice.

"You've got nerves of steel and such guts. Your heart's in the right place." He guided me into the hall, where a few campaign workers were standing around, looking sad. Poor Betty was among them. She had worked so hard but in vain.

Bob told me that I would be sharing a room with Bill Turner, the man who had been bullied by Jim Lyons. Turner occupied the top bunk and I was to sleep on the bottom bunk. "Your options will be open," said Bob mischievously.

Turner was lying face downwards, sobbing. I felt ill at ease, as

I always do when someone cries in front of me. In that way, I am like Nicky. I managed to utter some well-meaning but ill-chosen words:

"Don't take things too hard, comrade. There'll be another Election in about five years' time and more Elections after that. Who knows? Labour might win again."

"It's not that. It's that man," said Turner.

"What man?"

"Jim Lyons. He's a bully. He hasn't been doing his job and he hates Bob."

"You should have stood up to him and gone to Bob," I said sternly, adding, "The trouble with you is, you lack courage. If you'd stood up to Jim Lyons, Labour would probably have won."

Turner said nothing.

I got onto the lower bunk. My main concern was that I might talk in my sleep and reveal my guilty secret, namely that I had gone to London, where I had voted Conservative.

* * *

It was light by the time I was able to sleep. Later, after breakfast, we set off in a convoy of cars, followed by the campaign van. It was not unlike a funeral procession. Our destination was the Buckingham Town Hall, where the count in Bob's constituency was due to take place.

His supporters, including me, flocked into the market place outside the Buckingham Town Hall.

The unhappy crowd was angry and it had become vicious in places. I have always had something of the *tricoteuse* in me, and I got carried away, on the wave of mass hysteria and rage among my comrades. I edged my way through to the angriest section of the crowd.

A vibrant, rough, but extremely attractive man, whose name I have forgotten, flashed a jagged-toothed smile at me. His teeth were as white as snow. He was tall, well-built and dark-haired. He was brandishing a red flag with an intricately-embroidered hammer and sickle sewn onto it.

"Come on, El," said the man, "There's a fire escape at the side of the Town Hall. Go up to the roof, take the Union Jack down and replace it with the red flag, if you can."

The man knelt down and asked me to sit on his shoulders, enabling me to wave the red flag about in circles. I have always been unfit because I hate exercise. The only exercise I take is swimming across Marseille harbour, where I intend to have my ashes scattered. On this occasion, I wasn't nearly as unfit as I am today.

The man supporting me on his shoulders, encouraged me to continue to wave the red flag backwards and forwards. He started to sing *The Red Flag* and dozens joined him. The more loudly some of the Maxwell supporters sang this popular and engaging song, the more violent some of them became. The crowd was getting out of control and a few policemen stepped in. The man supporting me on his shoulders took me to the bottom of the fire escape at the side of the building. It consisted of metal steps.

"Grab hold of the red flag and take it up to the roof. Then remove the Union Jack and put up the red flag instead," repeated the man, adding, "Come on, comrade. I know you can do it!"

How I liked to be addressed as "comrade", even though my communist days were over!

I did as I was told and reached the roof of the building. I felt a surge of adrenalin.

"Put up the flag comrade! Put up the flag!" shouted the crowd in unison.

I made my way to the flagpole and got hold of the union flag which was very heavy. I managed to lift it from its birth, with a great effort and threw it from the roof onto the ground.

A woman aged about twenty-five, got out her cigarette lighter, poured an inflammatory substance onto the flag, and set it alight.

What I had been asked to do was difficult, because I was already exhausted, and a man's strength was needed to erect the red flag, which seemed much heavier now. I was able to wave it about in the air, though, as I had when I was on the man's shoulders.

I walked towards the edge of the roof and got a standing ovation. I continued to wave the red flag about. The terrific applause I was getting encouraged me to behave rebelliously. Little did these people know that I had voted Tory.

They all started to sing the fucking *"Internationale"*. I remembered this song from my communist days, and because I had resigned from the Party, I began to feel uneasy, but proud at the same time.

I heard a loud, male voice with a local accent calling my name over a loudhailer. I had no idea how this person knew my name. He was a policeman.

"Eleanor Berry, will you please come down," he shouted.

I suddenly got an attack of vertigo, which I hadn't suffered from until that moment. The policeman ordered me to come down once more but I felt horribly giddy. I couldn't find my way to the metal steps at the side of the building.

I was later told that someone in the crowd had spoken to Bob, who was still in the building. Whoever it was, this person must have advised him to come outside to use the loudhailer himself.

"Eleanor!" he shouted.

"Any more news, Bob?" I shouted back. My head was spinning and my vertigo was getting even worse.

By this time, Bob had known he had lost his seat, to the nondescript Tory candidate, Bill Benyon.

"Eleanor!" he shouted once more. He sounded a bit pissed off. "Do what the police are telling you to do. Come down immediately!"

"I'll try to come down, Bob, but I've got very bad vertigo. I'm giddy," I shouted back.

"If you suffer from vertigo, you shouldn't have gone up there in the first place. Stop being so naughty and do as you're told."

"I can't find the steps."

"What the hell do you mean, you can't find the steps?"

A foul-tempered policeman went up to the roof and took me down, using a fireman's lift. The procedure was really undignified.

Another policeman seized the red flag and threw it onto the ground. It landed at the bottom of the metal steps.

"Was you told to go up there and replace the union flag with a communist flag?" he asked.

"I can't remember."

"I don't believe you. Was it Mr Maxwell who told you to do so?"

"No, it wasn't!" I said assertively.

"Why did you do it, then?"

"Sorry, I got carried away."

"Where did you find the red flag?"

"A man I'd never met before, gave it to me."

"Oh, he did, did he? We don't 'alf come across some odd people these days," the policeman commented obscurely. He didn't press charges.

Bob got into the Labour Party campaign van, which was driven by Mr Hoppitt, once more. He stood up in the back of the van and boomed through the loudhailer to his supporters.

"Thank you all for your courageous and loyal support. We are disappointed but not down-hearted. We have lost a battle but not the war."

Ida and her mother were standing near the van. The two eccentric women roused everyone into singing, "*For he's a jolly good fellow*".

Bob, his son, Kevin, then aged ten, Arthur, Chris, Betty and I got into the van. Mr Hoppitt drove us to the Wharf House, so that Betty could clear everything out.

I helped her to do this. I assured her that there was absolutely no rivalry between us. We were both infatuated by the same man, but we were still fiercely united, like two soldiers in the trenches, fighting in the same war.

I very tactfully asked Betty's permission to take one of Bob's shirts from the chest of drawers. She graciously handed the shirt to me.

I've still got the shirt, with its sleeves extending nearly a yard beyond my hands. Sometimes, I wear it at breakfast, if I want to show off. Other times, I use it as a night-dress. Betty sang my favourite Edith Piaf song, *Padam*, which I intend to have sung at my cremation service. She rolled briefs and pairs of socks into balls and folded the remaining shirts. The clear-out took us about two hours. Betty put all the bags into her Jaguar and drove to Headington Hill Hall.

Bob, Arthur, Chris and I got into the campaign van, which was no longer driven by Mr Hoppitt, but by Chris. I sat in front, between him and Arthur. Bob sat in the back.

Chris drove the van down the streets which were inhabited mostly by Labour supporters. Occasionally, Bob rose to his feet, and called through the loudhailer, "We have lost a battle but not the war."

Occasionally, he held my hair (which was very long in those days) to steady himself when he kept sitting down and standing up. This gave me a fantastic buzz. Despite his defeat, I was inappropriately happy during the journey, being flanked by two charming men, with my favourite one holding my hair. Chris saw two Tories, walking down the street, wearing blue rosettes and laughing. He wound down his window and leant out.

"Bloody Tories! Let it drop in and pull the flaming chain!" he shouted vulgarly.

Bob said nothing. When I looked at him in the driver's mirror, I noticed he was smiling.

We returned to the Wharf House for lunch, although Betty had gone to Oxford. We went into Bob's study for drinks and found Bill Turner, the deputy agent in there, weeping. He walked towards Bob and put his arms round him. It was really embarrassing.

"I'm so ashamed of failing to stand up to Jim Lyons," muttered Turner.

"It's all right. It's all right," said Bob kindly.

However, after Turner had left the room and gone into the hall, on his way to the dining room, I could see from the expression on Bob's face, that he regarded the wretched man with pathos and disdain.

Bob frequently failed to get on with members of his own sex. I think I may have mentioned this before. He had a tendency to frighten them but he rarely did this to women.

"That poor man!" I said, turning to Bob. "It's obvious how much he looks up to you."

"I understand that but he's a bit gaga," Bob replied.

Lunch at the Wharf House was a very sad occasion. Ida and her mother had tears in their eyes throughout the meal. Bob looked forlorn, but cheered up a little when a glass of beer was passed to him. Jean Baddeley and Judy Ennals were also there, their heads lowered.

Those who had cars got into them, and returned to Headington Hill Hall. I had no idea what had happened to Mr Hoppitt. I was alone with Bob in the campaign van, which is what I wanted.

During the two hours it took to travel from the Wharf House to Headington Hill Hall, I had a very long conversation with Bob. It was unusual for anyone to have long conversations with him, because he found it difficult to form bridges between himself and others. This trait was shown in his handwriting analysis which I will be discussing later on in this book. He must have loved me very much to break this habit. In fact, I know he loved me.

He spoke first.

"Does Michael (my father, that is) disapprove of our relationship?" he asked.

"He's never mentioned it," I replied. "Do you think he finds it offensive in some way?"

"Yes."

"Why?" I asked.

"Because I'd find it offensive, if your father took this kind of interest in Isabel. I'd go round to his house and I'd put a stop to it." I laughed.

"My father doesn't mind at all," I said. "He's got nothing to disapprove of, if that's what you mean."

"Do you think Michael likes me?" asked Bob suddenly. He sounded almost childlike.

"Yes, of course he likes you," I replied. "Why shouldn't he like you?"

There was a short silence, which was broken by Bob. He changed the subject.

"You once told me that you were disturbed by Gorki's novel, *Foma Gordyev*. Why did a book like that hit you so hard?" he asked.

"It is very morbid in places. Sometimes, morbidity turns me on. Other times, it distresses me," I said.

As I see it now, *Foma Gordyev* is a repetitive, rambling book about barges combing the Volga, in late nineteenth century Russia, and the rowdy behaviour of merchants aboard them.

Looking back on the book, Foma, the main protagonist, really is a most awful drip, who cannot relate to others, and who continuously passes namby-pamby remarks, such as, "I'm afraid I haven't really got used to life yet."

He bumbles about, boozing, attacking members of his own class, and for want of better words, is a shambling pain in the butt.

Perhaps the book obsessed me at a very young age, because of its rich language and its generally vibrant tone, regardless of Foma's effete nihilism.

Extensive coverage is given to the appearance and function of the engines of the barges combing the Volga, not that this is relevant to the plot, but I thought I'd mention it all the same.

Also, there is acutely morbid and fatalistic narrative in the early part of the book, particularly when Max Gorki describes the death and funeral of Foma's father.

"I don't understand why the book disturbed you so much," said Bob.

"It haunted and tormented me," I said.

"It haunted you? Why did it haunt you?"

I was shouting because I was getting carried away.

"Will you please stop shouting," said Bob, adding, "You've been shouting ever since you got into this van."

I wasn't considerate enough to take the loss of Bob's seat on board, or indeed the annihilation of almost all his family during the Holocaust. I went on shouting, as I told him about some of the events described in *Foma Gordyev*. I couldn't stop shouting because I wanted to exorcise something which I couldn't quite understand.

"Foma Gordyev is the book's main character," I explained, "He's the wealthy son of a barge owner who dies in moribund circumstances in front of his son. He dies while drinking tea on the lawn outside their house. Apples fall from an overhead tree into his tea, just before he takes his last breath."

I studied Bob's profile. He was looking very attractive but baffled. I continued, "His father dies suddenly on a warm autumn morning."

"I'm absolutely riveted," said Bob, "go on."

"Foma's father has a Russian Orthodox funeral and lies in an open coffin. Foma is asked to kiss his father, after his death, from which he never completely recovers.

"He turns into a permanently intoxicated wreck. Although he is wealthy, he despises the gluttony of his own class."

Bob cleared his throat loudly.

"What did I say about your shouting?" he asked irritably.

"Oh, sorry." I lowered the tone of my voice. "The book describes the deterioration of Foma's mind, and the worsening of his addiction to alcohol."

"What did I say about your shouting?" repeated Bob.

"Shouting?"

"Yes, shouting. I've told you before to stop shouting, so why are you continuing to do so?"

"Sorry, I won't do it again, Bob."

"Have you got anything more to say about the contents of that book?" he asked.

"Oh, yes. Towards the end, there's a description of Foma's drunken words spoken in rage about the greed of his fellow merchants. He uses wonderful language. He says, '*Even hell is too good a place for swine like you! Not in clean flames, but in sizzling dung ought you to be scorched, tormented for centuries on end!*' You should have used these words when speaking to Jim Lyons."

Bob laughed. I continued, "When they heard Foma's words, the merchants couldn't think of anything constructive to do, so they tied him up and sent for his godfather."

"Blimey! When the hell's this story going to end?" asked Bob.

"The book's ending is an anti-climax," I said. "Foma staggers about drunk, claiming to be a prophet, and someone who bumps into him in the street says, 'Ha! Ha! A prophet, indeed!'"

"Is that the lot?" asked Bob hopefully.

"You remind me of my maternal grandfather, F. E. Smith who died in 1930. Someone was telling him an interminable story in a restaurant. F. E. Smith called for a waiter and said, "Waiter, will you listen to the end of this gentleman's story, please.""

"It sounds as if F. E. Smith had a good point," said Bob.

"I had a morbid fascination for Russian literature and all things Russian, when I was much younger," I said.

"I don't think you were getting these whacky thoughts because of that book alone, or indeed because of Russian literature in general," Bob began. "I think Pamela (my mother) played a large part in your feeling out of sorts at the time. I know she's a very bossy, domineering woman. I don't think parents should be bossy or domineering towards their children."

There was another silence.

"Is she still shoving you?" he asked. "I know I once asked you this before."

"She did so when I was little. Now, I've learnt how to handle her. We get on all right now," I replied. I changed the subject. "I'll tell you something which might make you laugh," I added. "My housemistress called me into her study once, and said, 'It has been brought to my attention that you sing the Russian National Anthem in your bath.'"

"*Did* you sing the Russian National Anthem in your bath?" asked Bob. He sounded confused, rather than amused.

"Yes, I did. Oh, I forgot to tell you, the father went into his son's room and told him he was about to die."

Bob swerved to avoid a pedestrian.

"Whose bloody father?" he asked impatiently.

"Why, Foma Gordyev's father, of course."

"You seem to be very preoccupied with death. I think you lost someone whom you loved very much. Is that what happened?" Bob asked sympathetically.

"No."

"I think I know why that book disturbed you so much. I'm familiar with it. You certainly don't advertise it very interestingly. You found it beautifully written and pure. You read it over and over again, and in comparison with the book, you found that your own life was humdrum and sad. You're rather a lonely person aren't you?"

"Sometimes, I am. Not always."

"You certainly came out of yourself when you were working for me. Everyone liked you being around. You spend too much time on your own, though you need company. I know what loneliness is like. I'm going to write a book about it one day," said Bob.

There was a silence which was broken by Bob. "I think it's time you got married," he said assertively.

"Well, er, well, I'm not quite ready yet," I said guardedly.

"To make a marriage work, you have to give as much as you take. Which are you, a giver or a taker?"

"I'd say I was both of these," I said abruptly. "Most of us are."

"Sometimes, I think you would have been far happier if you had been born a male," said Bob obscurely.

I laughed. There was another silence.

"Are you still seeing that fellow, Dr Goldman?" he asked.

"Occasionally. Just to get flu injections and prescriptions for antibiotics," I lied.

"I didn't get on at all well with him, as you know. He called me a 'crook' and I called him a 'quack.'"

"I had an unfortunate experience in Dr Goldman's rooms once," I said.

"What happened?"

"I said to a woman, whom I thought was a new receptionist, 'My God, that man, Goldman, is attractive. He must come like the Volga!'"

"Will you kindly keep your opinion to yourself, and wait in the waiting room, if you don't mind!" said the woman angrily.

"I approached Dr Goldman's secretary, and said, 'Who is that disagreeable new receptionist? Is she an agency temp?'"

"No," said the secretary. "She is Dr Goldman's wife."

Bob let out the guttural Cossack's laugh for which he was well-known.

"That's what you might call putting your foot in it," he said mildly.

"I hear this Goldman fellow is always hitting other doctors!" said Bob. (Nicky must have told him this.)

"My father consults Dr Goldman," I said, "but sometimes he consults his locum whose name is Dr Creightmore. Dr Creightmore, charges far less than Dr Goldman, and there is often terrible animosity between the two doctors."

"My father was in the London Clinic, following a hip

replacement. Dr Creightmore was in the room, talking to my father who had a bottle of whisky on his bedside table.

Dr Goldman came into the room, blustered towards the bedside table, and seized the bottle of whisky.

He then gave Dr Creightmore a thunderous slap on the ear and shouted, "How dare you allow him this, you brainless nincompoop, when I've just saved his liver!"

Bob laughed once more. This was uncharacteristic of him as he didn't particularly like anecdotes.

The remainder of the conversation between us took place in Russian.

The only trouble was, Bob did not correct me when I made mistakes. He asked me (in Russian) what I had been reading recently.

"Dostoevsky, Gogol and Chekhov," I replied, quoting the first names which came to my head. I refrained from telling him that I had been reading the works of these writers in English.

As yet, I hadn't confessed to Bob that I had resigned from the Communist Party, partly because Lenin had failed to keep the promises which he had made in his Manifesto, although I had many other reasons for resigning, as I mentioned earlier.

I fell asleep for the rest of the journey. Bob woke me up when we reached Headington Hill Hall.

Oping, the Filipino cook, carried my suitcase into the hall. Bob was exhausted. He went upstairs and slept until dinner-time.

Ghislaine appeared from nowhere and pointed to her suitcase. I think she had been staying with her cousins, the Rosens.

"Will you take my suitcase up to my room, please," she said to me.

"Indeed, I'll do nothing of the sort! I'm not your maid. Who on earth do you think you are?" I said, my voice raised, adding, "Perhaps, you would like me to go up to London and buy you a present,"

"O.K.," she said meekly. "Will you come up to my room and push me on my rocking horse, please?"

"If you behave yourself, I might just consider doing so."

I granted her request.

While I was pushing her, she said, "I don't think you're Labour at all. I think you're a Conservative."

"Why does the young lady say that?" I asked.

"You went to London on Polling Day, didn't you?"

"If you say so."

"When you got to London, you voted Conservative. You've got a very Conservative-sounding voice."

"You can think what you want, you impertinent little brat!"

"Just tell me. I won't tell anyone. Did you vote Conservative?"

"No," I lied. "Anyway, it's dinner-time."

Kevin, aged ten and one of Ghislaine's older brothers, came into the bedroom and said that dinner had started. He briefed me on what was being discussed at dinner. There was a clinical formality in the way he spoke and he had a dry sense of humour. He was intellectually advanced for a ten-year-old boy. His speech was sharp, intuitive and concise.

"You're late," said Bob confrontationally, as I sat down on the vacant chair on his left side.

"Yes, I know. Ghislaine told me to push her on her rocking-horse."

"It's not Ghislaine who gives the orders in this house. It's her father," said Bob. I could tell that the loss of his seat was only just getting to him. He was low in spirits. I felt sorry for him.

"Sorry, Bob," I said.

Ghislaine came into the dining-room, wearing pyjamas and helped herself to some chicken, which she brought to the table in her hand. She walked over to her father's chair and asked him to pull a wish-bone with her. She got the wish and he asked her what it was.

"I hope you win next time," she said sweetly. He took her on his knee and caressed her. This made me exceptionally jealous. I had always been insanely jealous of Ghislaine, mainly because she had been beaten by her father. I think I've mentioned this before.

The entire family were at the table. When Bob was subdued, it was not uncommon for his children to be infected by his mood. Sometimes, he asked members of his family very startling questions.

On a later occasion, I was the recipient of one of these questions, but I always barked my reply and that made Bob laugh.

There had been a debate on the television about the Common Market. One of the participants said he favoured the country's integration into a united Europe. Bob turned to me.

"Does that support your view, Eleanor?" he asked.

"No, it certainly does not!" I replied, my voice raised. "The nation would be robbed of its individuality, and it would become a mere county within a soulless state."

Bob looked a bit stunned by the aggressive tone of my voice. Then he smiled. "I liked that," he said eventually.

To get back to dinner at Headington Hill Hall on the evening after the Election, the children chatted among themselves for a while, until Betty entered the conversation.

"What are we going to do about that heinous man, Jim Lyons, Papa?" she asked. "Not only has he lost you your seat through sheer idleness; he has also bullied and persecuted a decent, conscientious man who is absolutely devoted to you, and has caused him to crack up."

"I ought to have sent Eleanor round to his house. She would have scared the wits out of him!" said Bob.

Within a few minutes, dinner was over.

Bob, Betty and the children got up and left the diningroom. They all looked dejected.

* * *

For the first and I think only time during our relationship, I received a bite from Bob.

Later that evening, he invited me to watch an American thriller with him. He took me upstairs to a room with a television in it. The room was known as the "bird room". It was called the "bird room", because it contained a number of porcelain birds of different colours and sizes.

Bob turned the television on and sat on the sofa. I sat on the floor at his feet. The film was totally incomprehensible but he appeared to understand it and found it extremely gripping.

Even when my wits are at their best, I find American accents hard to understand.

I asked Bob a lot of questions.

"Who's that man?"

Silence.

"Is that the woman he's been taking out?"

Silence.

"Is that the woman's sister?"

Silence.

"What did she say?"

Those were not the only questions I asked Bob. I asked him about twenty questions in all.

It was at that point that I received the bite which I mentioned earlier.

"For Christ's sake, shut up!" he shouted.

* * *

The following morning, I put on a red leather mini-dress and high-heeled, snakeskin boots which covered part of my thighs. After breakfast in the kitchen, I went into Bob's study. He seemed delighted to see me, either because of my apparel or my personality, possibly both. "I like the boots," he said.

I was due to go to my parents' house in Buckinghamshire that morning. Mr Brightwell was waiting for me in the drive.

I said "goodbye" to Betty and I thanked her for all her kindness. Then, I said "goodbye" to Bob.

"I'm going to miss you," he said.

"I'm going to miss you, too," I replied banally.

"I want you to come to this house, whenever you feel like it. You have a permanent invitation, even if you only want to call for one of your baths. You will write to me, won't you?"

"Of course, I will, Bob. You're very kind. I really don't want to leave," I said.

"I'm not kind! There are a lot of untrustworthy people about, who will only be interested in you because your father owns two national newspapers.

"I'm not like that," he continued. "I take you for what you are like as a person and any time you have a problem, let me know. When you come back, we'll read *Pravda* together." He added, "Thank you for all your hard work. We've helped each other. I've helped you to become more assertive, and you've gone out of your way, to help me to retain my seat, even though I didn't win."

I felt very sad at the prospect of leaving Headington Hill Hall. I got into Mr Brightwell's car. Bob waved goodbye, until the car was out of sight.

Once I arrived at my parents' house, I went into the library and wrote a letter to Bob. This time, I wrote to him in English. My letter was very affectionate and even loving in places.

I said I didn't regard him as a boss, but as a close friend. Added to that, I said some fairly intimate things, including how very attractive I thought he was.

The letter was about two hundred words long. Unfortunately, I failed to keep a copy of it.

Within about a week, I received a reply.

Dear Eleanor,

How very nice of you to write to me the way you did about my defeat in the General Election.

I would gladly have put pen to paper, instead of dictating this note, if only my handwriting were a bit more legible.

I am terribly grateful for your help during the Election campaign. I know everybody enjoyed having you there.

Yours ever,
Bob

* * *

Within a short period of time, I gained a driving licence and my father gave me a Mini Clubman Estate. It was Nicky who had persuaded him to give me a car.

I drove to Headington Hill Hall in the autumn. I had invited myself for the weekend. I arrived on Friday evening.

"Why didn't you tell me Eleanor was coming to stay?" said Bob to Betty. "I would have been able to look forward to seeing her again." He often uttered these words.

It's on remembering remarks like that, that I become very angry when I hear anyone criticizing Bob. The ordeal I had to suffer was even worse after his death, than in his lifetime, because the gutter press took unfair advantage of the fact that the dead can't sue for libel. I know Bob was not entirely a saint, but I will not hear a word against him, whatever his faults may have been.

The next day, Bob took me for a walk round the garden, which was covered with dead leaves. We spoke Russian once more. The swimming pool was no longer in use. Its leaf-covered water was an uninviting shade of green.

Suddenly, he picked me up, held me over the water and threatened to drop me in. The incident showed the prankish side of his nature, which manifested itself whenever he wanted to become the boy, who had been deprived of clothes, food, toys and jokes during his phenomenally unhappy childhood. Not only that, the Nazis had murdered almost his family the members.

Bob took me to his study, adjoining the drawing room. Jean was there, awaiting her boss's instructions. She and I greeted each other. We had always got on well, despite her maddening bath rota during the election.[10*]

"How many people have died in the constituency, Jean?" asked Bob.

"Four. The letters to the next of kin are ready for you to sign."

"Good. Have there been any marriages, so that the couples can be congratulated?"

"Yes. Just one. The couple are ex-circus performers. The husband works in a shop now."

"His name?"

"Cyril Dibbs. He's a dwarf."

Bob sat back in his executive leather chair and lit a cigar.

"Is his wife also a dwarf?" he asked.

"Yes, Mr Maxwell."

"Blimey, some like it hot!" said Bob obscurely.

* * *

The Maxwells employed a most extraordinary butler. I don't know his real name, but Bob always addressed him, in irony, as "Genius", because he was proverbially slow-witted. I'll refer to him as "Genius" whenever I write about him, to avoid confusion. I don't think he was English.

Genius came into my bedroom at eight o'clock one Saturday morning, having failed to knock on the door. I didn't have a stitch on.

"Are there any empty glasses in here?" asked Genius.

"No, I'm getting ready for breakfast. I'm not dressed," I replied.

"I think I may have made a mistake," he said mildly.

"Oh, yes, you certainly have!"

10* Jean claimed that she had never had an affair with Bob. His son, Ian, however, thinks that they may have had an isolated fling.

Poor old Genius! I thought it would have been unfair to report him to his bosses, because he would have been fired, and it might have been hard for him to find employment elsewhere, given the time of year.

Bob's son, Ian, with whom I am very friendly, told me an exceptionally amusing story.

On Genius's first day of employment with the Maxwells, he somehow managed to sever an artery on his wrist, with a recently-sharpened meat cleaver. No-one knows whether this was a suicide attempt or an accident.

Blood was spurting out all over the place, in rhythm to his heart beat. It got all over one of his boss's best suits. If a practical bystander hadn't stopped the bleeding, Genius would have died.

Bob passed a remark and as always, he failed to mince his words,

"You are very brave but you are also very stupid!" It was after that incident that Bob insisted on calling him "Genius."

Although it was a Saturday, Bob was interviewing a blonde secretary in his study. Kevin entered the room, with a glass of red wine in his hand, mistaking the blonde woman, who had her back to him, for me.

"Have a glass of wine," he said exuberantly. "Vintage Château de Sade!"

"Fuck off, Kevin!" said Bob.

Kevin was then about eleven. He had the mental age of a sixteen-year-old.

"I liked the sexy blonde secretary you were interviewing this morning, Dad," said Ian at lunch. "She's much prettier than the one with the acne and the awful legs."

"I don't want to hear that kind of talk, Ian. It's cruel," Bob said.

"Sorry, Dad.

"So am I."

I admit I did not distinguish myself at Headington Hill Hall, the following day, which was a Sunday. I had been writing a vehement letter of complaint to someone who had crossed my path. I can't remember the details but I had spent most of the night and the whole morning on the job.

I came downstairs at about 12.45 shortly before lunch and bumped into Bob who was walking across the hall.

"Hullo. I hear you got up very early this morning," he said in irony, adding "Do you realize the maid wasn't able to get in to make the bed?"

I could tell he was cross. I smiled, took his hand in mine and rolled my recently made-up eyes at him.

"Forgive me, Bob," I said.

"All right. Naughty Pussycat. Come next door and help yourself to a gin and tonic."

The entire family were in the drawingroom. Bob insisted that all his children come to Headington Hill Hall for Sunday lunch every week.

Jean came into the room, to remind her boss that he was due to go out on business that afternoon, even though it was a Sunday. He was wearing a red and white pin-striped suit, which was so loud, it could have been heard in Algeria.

"Mr Maxwell," Jean commanded, "I'm not going anywhere with you, until you change into a more appropriate suit!"

"All right, all right, Jean. I'm fed up with being ordered about by a bunch of hens," said Bob.

* * *

I invited myself to Headington Hill Hall in a few weeks' time. I went out for a walk in the garden. Ghislaine, Bob's youngest and apparently his favourite child, ran towards me. She was about ten years old.

"Will you take me out for a ride in your new car?" she asked.

"Not now, I won't. It's nearly lunch-time," I replied, adding,

"I may take you out after lunch but not without your father's express permission."

"I'm sure he'll give his permission. Oh, by the way, Daddy said you're not to play Beethoven's *Ode to Joy* when you drive. He said you have a lot of accidents, drive too fast and deliberately crash into the backs of other cars, when you listen to it. Otherwise, he said you're not too bad a driver."

"That's damned decent of you!"

She didn't reply straight away. She was looking pretty and sultry with her long, brown pony-tail and large, almond-shaped eyes. She smiled charmingly.

"I do hope Daddy will let me come out with you after lunch, as long as you promise not to listen to Beethoven. I don't want to end up in a ditch."

"You'll end up in a manure heap, if you don't stop being so damned cheeky!" I replied.

* * *

Just before yet another of Bob's General Election campaigns, I had been without a car. Even my late brother, Adrian, had forbidden me to drive his car, when taking Labour Party supporters to the polls.

I had smashed up my own car, while I was driving Bob's cook, Oping to London. I was listening to Beethoven's *Ode to Joy* and was so stimulated by the beautiful piece, that I crashed my car into another vehicle in front of me, on purpose. Oping was scared out of her wits.

The love of my life, Peachey, now tragically dead, only had an Austin hearse at his disposal. He needed it to carry all his things in. Because of my taste for the macabre, I insisted that he drive a hearse, instead of an ordinary van.

I told him I desperately needed the hearse,, although I didn't give him a reason. I would add that he was a Tory and would not have approved of my working for Labour.

I drove the hearse to Headington Hill Hall and parked it just outside the pillars, under which Bob kept his Rolls. I rang the bell and Oping, who had made a good recovery from her shock, opened it. Bob came out of the house and I greeted him. He soon noticed what I had parked in his drive.

"It's your choice of vehicle I'm not too confident about," he said mildly.

"It's perfect for driving your supporters to the polls, Bob. I could fit at least ten people in the back at a time. All I'll have to do is take the bier pins out."

"I strictly forbid you to leave the bloody thing anywhere in my constituency. I'm trying to win this fucking Election for Christ's sake!" said Bob.

* * *

Bob often met my father in London.

"How's that smashing daughter of yours, Michael?" he said on one of these occasions. Once, when he saw Nicky in London, he told him he was my surrogate father. He also told him, on two occasions, that he could see himself in me.

I tried, without success, to work out what he meant.

I always looked forward to my weekends at Headington Hill Hall. The Maxwell family had gathered together for Sunday lunch once more.

Bob was in rather a low mood that day. Because of his memories of his childhood, and the loss of nearly all his original family during the Holocaust, he suffered from pronounced mood swings, which worsened as he got older.

I think it can be said that he was bi-polar. I will discuss this matter, later on in this book, when I will comment on Bob's handwriting analysis, which I had performed.

Added to Bob's black mood that day, was the fact that Genius, his raving mad butler, had found it extremely difficult to tell the difference between red wine and port. He poured port into the family's high-stemmed, intricately decorated Venetian glasses.

"Oh, no, no, no, no, Genius!" shouted Bob. "This is port. I want red wine!"

Genius left the room and produced a bottle of red wine and a tray of clean glasses.

The unfortunate butler bungled yet again. He brought in a bottle of cheap red wine, when Bob had wanted a more costly bottle. The crate of expensive wine had been delivered to the house by a friend of the family.

Bob was furious.

"Oh, no, no, no, no, Genius!" he repeated.

"I'm sorry, Mr Maxwell, I am unable to understand your instructions," ventured Genius.

"Just take away the bottle you brought in, and the glasses, and start again. Bring in some *Rosé*, this time," ordered Bob obscurely.

The Maxwell children looked subdued, Ian most of all. He hated witnessing one of his father's depressions.

It's impossible to believe what Genius did next. He brought in yet another tray of Venetian glasses and put them on the table. First, he filled the glasses half-full with white wine. Then, he added red wine, making it look as if the glasses had been filled with *Rosé*. His boss was incandescent with rage. He stormed out of the room. My father was very amused when I told him the story.

I stayed with the Maxwells once more. This time, I was asked to arrive in time for dinner on Saturday evening.

I sat next to Bob at dinner. He turned to me suddenly.

"I had your mother here for lunch today," he said confrontationally.

"Did you now?" I replied.

"You look exactly like her, except for your hair colour and difference in age. You both have the same coloured eyes, and the same bone structure. You're very beautiful, although, inevitably she looks older than you."

"Indeed?"

"She behaved very badly when she was here."

"Oh, dear, what did she do?"

"She was very aggressive. She quarrelled with everyone at the table. She also hit someone on the head with her table napkin."

"Did she quarrel with Betty or your children?"

"No. I had invited three friends of mine, all Labour Party people. She accused them of orchestrating the printers' strikes on *The Daily Telegraph*. She even attacked me, which was out of order, because it was I who had negotiated with the printers, and had urged them to call off one of their strikes."

"I really am terribly sorry," I said. "My mother is quite mad and can be a pain in the butt at times. She just loves having rows with people."

"Yes, she certainly does. She generated an atmosphere of unrest throughout my household. In the end, I told her to go upstairs and sit in the bird room."

My mother looked at one of the photograph albums in the bird room. It contained nothing but chest X-rays, from cover to cover.

Bob came up to see her after lunch to complain about her behaviour. He asked her what she was doing.

"I'm looking at these chest X-rays. I really do find this *awfully* odd," she said in the loud, shrill voice characteristic of her.

The chest X-rays related to Bob, who had had a cankerous lung removed, when he was younger.

"Don't you dare, ever again, behave like this in my house! It's not fair on Eleanor," he shouted.

"Why do you think she behaved so badly?" I asked.

"Because she sees me as a baby-snatcher," said Bob.

* * *

Bob's mood swings ranged from playful euphoria to impenetrable gloom, due to the Holocaust and the gassing of most of his family.

His original name was Jan Ludvig Hoch or Abrahim Leib Hoch.

His greatest love was for his mother, whose name was Hannah Hoch. I may have mentioned this earlier. According to the picture I saw of her, she closely resembled Isabel, except that she was stouter.

In the picture, she was wearing a simple, dark-coloured dress, with a large collar, made of the same material. She had a very kind face and a look of *Mona Lisa* serenity about her. I have a photograph of her in my flat. When visitors ask me who she is, I like to refer to her as "Our Lady'.

Bob was her favourite and youngest child. There were other children as well. I can imagine him running behind his mother, clinging to her skirts. She too, was sent to the gas chambers.

"I love hiding behind ladies' petticoats," Bob said to me at lunch one day, when he was in a good mood.

"I'm a very happy person." he once said (on television), towards the end of his life. I suspect he was being economical with the truth.

There is a Russian proverb, "*Happiness is not a horse. It cannot be harnessed*".

When Bob made the remark on television, he was merely going through a phase of being contented. His "happiness" so called was by no means static at that time of his life.

When he was quite a young man and was happily married, he was living at Headington Hill Hall. Despite the tragic losses of his son, Michael, his daughter, Karine and, of course, most members of his previous family, Bob was reasonably contented and optimistic. He was hopelessly in love with Betty and was delighted to be the father of his new family. Also, his publishing business was going well and his finances were in good shape.

It was when he was older that his "happiness" so called diminished. He had been crossed in love, by his favourite secretary and was feeling very lonely. He was pathologically jealous of Ghislaine's boyfriends. He was very overweight and was exhausted for most of the time. Also, through no fault of hers, he had begun to fall out of love with Betty and he was no longer happy at Headington Hill Hall. Instead, he stayed at the *Mirror*.

On many occasions, when he was older, say in his late sixties, he rarely spoke at meals and seldom welcomed any conversational overtures. I can always tell when someone near me is depressed, whether they show it or not.

The occasion I will refer to now, was on the Saturday, just after Bob had won £50,000, having successfully sued the satirical magazine, *Private Eye*. During the court case, he was reminded, for some reason, of Adolf Eichmann, the notorious Nazi who had been responsible for the gassing of most members of his original family. He was reduced to tears during the court case, particularly when his barrister mentioned the fact that Montgomery had pinned the Military Cross to his chest for bravery on the battlefield.

I was sitting on his right side at lunch and I decided not to speak to him until he spoke to me. I have always found it hard to handle a depressed person.

Most members of his family were at Headington Hill Hall. Lunch was almost silent. I felt sad on seeing Bob looking so downhearted. He had put on some weight, although his looks were still intact.

He suddenly turned to me, "Tell me, Eleanor, when you're not looking ravishingly beautiful, how do you occupy your time?"

I thanked him but he only wanted to hear a concise answer.

"I am a temporary medical secretary. I work for agencies who send me to London hospitals, where I type letters from consultants to G.P.s. Sometimes, I attend post mortems, where I take notes during autopsies."

"No gory talk, please," said Bob, "I'm eating." It seemed that he was at the bottom of a well. I knew he was thinking about the Nazis.

"Papa, she's been doing this kind of work for years and years," said Betty to her husband across the table. "Do you know what she said? She complained bitterly because she'd been out of work for two whole days. I had to laugh."

"I don't see why," said Bob. "Two whole days are two days lost."

"I went for an interview recently," I said. "I was applying for a job, working for a consultant at St Thomas's Hospital.

"He was a weirdo. He asked me if I was happy."

"'No, of course I'm not happy, you bloody fool! I'm out of work, aren't I?'" I shouted.

Bob laughed out loud. He was so amused, that it seemed as if my story had lifted his depression.

"How much are you earning?" he asked. (I was getting £9.50 an hour at that time.)

"I get £13.50 an hour," I lied. "I wouldn't settle for less than that."

"Good. You could take us all out to dinner at the Ritz with that," he remarked.

I was feeling much better because it appeared that Bob's black mood had lifted, due to the fact that I had made him laugh.

"Bob, will you give me a signed copy of your book, about the *Private Eye* case, entitled *Malice in Wonderland*, please?" I asked.

"I don't see why not, Eleanor. You very kindly gave me a signed copy of *Never Alone With Rex Malone*. Do you remember?"

"I don't forget the titles of my books easily," I said.

Bob laughed once more.

"Of course, I'll sign it for you – as one author to another," he said.

However, he got up from the table in the middle of lunch and called Kevin.

"Come on, Kevin, there's work to be done," he said, and went from the dining room in the drawing room.

I feared Bob would forget my request, after his conversation with Kevin. I followed him but he tried to shut the door in my face. I confess that I was aided by an extra dose of happy pills, which I had taken before lunch and which totally wiped out my inhibitions. I don't take them any more, because the only doctor prepared to prescribe them, has retired and has gone to live abroad. I may have mentioned this before.

Bob was very surprised by the fact that I had tried to follow him so vehemently. "Goodbye!" he said forcefully.

"Will you stop saying 'goodbye!'" I said. "You promised to sign my copy of your book. I've never known you to break a promise."

"Goodbye!" he repeated.

"I won't tolerate this, Bob, All I want is your signature."

"Leave Kevin and me alone!" he said, his voice raised.

"Indeed, I will *not* leave Kevin and you alone. When am I going to get a copy of your book?"

Bob was still concentrating his energies on his conversation with Kevin.

"Oh, come on, Bob!" I said. The happy pills I had taken had caused me to hit Jupiter, as they did at his birthday party, to be described later on in this book.

I pulled him by the tie, while his dumbfounded family looked on. They had followed me into the drawing room.

"I'm not leaving your house, until you give me a copy of your book!" I shouted. We had a fight.

Suddenly, Bob's personality mutated. No-one had pulled him by the tie before in his life. No-one had dared to do so. His stern facial features turned into a smile. "By God, I like your resistance! No-one has ever done this to me before," he said mildly, "Of course, I will sign the book for you. Just before he picked it up from his desk to sign, he asked me to do a pirouette while he watched. (I was wearing yellow trousers and a white sweater.)

"You look absolutely smashing!" he said.

I felt really strange on witnessing his extreme changes in mood. Sometimes he was ecstatic. Other times he was almost suicidal.

There is a passage in Betty's book, *A Mind of My Own*, which states that I was the only person who brought out the best in Robert Maxwell. Ian told me this at dinner recently.

* * *

I returned to Headington Hill Hall once more. Bob was in an exceptionally good mood. It was a hot summer's day and we were eating outside on the lawn. There was no umbrellas. It was stifling.

It was a small party, consisting of Betty, Jean, Bob and myself.

"I hear you spend a lot of your spare time dining with Sloane Rangers," Bob said suddenly.

I *hate* Sloane Rangers, Bob!" I protested.

"There's a man coming to see me this afternoon, who's writing a book about Sloane Rangers. He wants me to publish it. Would you like to meet him?"

"Oh, Christ, do I have to?" I said.

"I liked that!" said Bob. He gave his guttural Cossack's laugh. He told me he liked feisty, precocious women.

Jean, who was in charge of everything in the house and the offices, entered the conversation and talked about sheets, pillow-cases and towels.

"I don't want to hear about sheets, pillow-cases and towels," said Bob. "I want to hear about Eleanor's adventures. Come on, Eleanor, let's hear about them, the more outrageous the better!"

There was a large, thin, grey dog running round the table. His name was "Angora" and he belonged to Ghislaine. He was named after a Czechoslovakian river.

Genius was away on this occasion. He had had to go to a funeral. Once we were seated, Bob wolf-whistled for Oping, the cook. I laughed out loud.

"What are you laughing at?" asked Bob.

"I love the way you whistle. My sister can whistle like that but I can't."

Oping began to pass food round the table.

It amused me very much when Angora got between her legs and brought her onto the grass. There were peas, carrots, new potatoes and slices of boiled fish all over the place. I laughed out loud, although I shouldn't have done so.

"Do you think we could get the dog out?" said Bob mildly.

Jean continued to speak about sheets, pillow-cases and towels, although Bob had told her not to do so.

"I don't want to hear another word about that sort of thing!" he said, impatiently. "I'd much rather hear about Eleanor's adventures," he repeated, "Come on, Eleanor, let's hear some of your stories, for comic relief."

I did my best to amuse Bob and tried to hide the fact that I hadn't slept the night before. I told him the following:

"My first job was that of a nanny, but I was sacked after ten minutes." (I will mention the nanny job later on in this book.)

"Why?" asked Bob.

"Oh, no reason. Then I found work as a verbal interpreter in a National Health hospital in London. I was using French and Russian. I couldn't pull this off though. I lost my head and shouted at the parties concerned. Finally, I was bunged out."

Bob liked my use of the words, "bunged out" and laughed.

I continued, "Then I took shorthand for a team of pathologists. A senior secretary, a PA, who worked in the office next door to mine asked me to take her blazer to the cleaners."

"I wouldn't like to have been her. What the hell did you say to her, *Basso Profundo*?" asked Bob.

"I said, 'My contract states that I am a medical secretary, not a whipping boy or a servant. I will *not* take your blazer to the cleaners."

"Christ turned the other cheek, so why didn't you?" asked Bob, who was expressing an attitude which for him, was totally out of character. He adhered vehemently to Judaism, as opposed to Christianity

"Christ died young," I said, perhaps unwisely. Bob tilted his head backwards, which he always did when he was shocked or embarrassed. I made sure that my reply was not offensive to him in any way.

"Let's have some more stories, but for Christ's sake, keep them brief," said Bob, adding, "Tell us about that time when you were arrested in Brighton, for breaking a window belonging to W. H. Smith & Son's."

"How did you know about that?" I asked.

"I have my spies. Come on, tell me what happened."

"I went to W. H. Smith & Son's in Churchill Square, Brighton, to buy some books. I was at Sussex University at the time. The Manager of the shop said he was about to close. He accepted payment for the books but he refused to give me a plastic bag to carry them in, although it was pouring with rain.

"I left, carrying the books. I was so furious that I kicked in a pane of glass belonging to the shop. I went on kicking until the glass broke. The Manager, who was very fit, caught up with me, when I tried to get away." Bob cleared his throat. I continued, "I had to appear in a magistrates' court the next day.

"The magistrate banged on and on about my need to attend anger management classes. I interrupted him, 'Oh, do shut up and just tell me how much I owe you!' I said."

Bob laughed convulsively. I was overjoyed.

"The magistrate was pretty pissed off. He named the sum, whatever it was.

"I got out my cheque book and said: 'All right. Who do I make this out to?'"

"You don't write out a cheque in the dock! You go downstairs to the front office," said the magistrate irritably.

"You should have produced a pile of dog-eared bank notes when you were in the dock," said Bob. "Let's have another story."

My agency sent me to the personnel department at the Middlesex Hospital in London, one Monday morning. The personnel manager casually told me that she had double-booked me. She told me to go home."

"I hope you hit her on the head with your shoe," remarked Bob.

"I should have done so. Instead, I said, 'Would you say that to a taxi driver?'

"No," she said.

"I'm sure you wouldn't. Shall I tell you why?"

"Why?" she asked.

"Because a taxi driver would have your throat. So would I if had a knife."

"So you went back the next day with your knife?" began Bob.

Oping came to the table to tell Bob that a call had come through from Moscow. Gorbachev was on the line.

Bob left the table and I felt dejected because I had been deprived of my audience. I have always needed an audience, just as a Chinaman needs rice.

* * *

I completed the manuscript of *Never Alone with Rex Malone* in the summer of 1985. The book opened in the year 2054, and then looked back to the late twentieth century, when Bob and Betty, referred to as "Rex Malone" and "Hortense Malone" respectively, were the most revered couple in Britain. Rex Malone was not only Prime Minister but was also a god-like figure. Indeed, cleaners of his tomb actually prayed to him.

A thuggish, sex-crazed funeral director, called Natalie Klein, was in love with Rex Malone and fought ruthlessly for him in his quest to become Prime Minister, in any way she could.

Obviously, I couldn't have sent the manuscript to a publisher, until Bob had found out about its existence and read it.

I feared he wouldn't allow me to get the book published, because of the ribaldry, morbidity, necrophilia and extreme black humour which peppered its pages, even though he was the central figure.

I asked my unfortunate father to read the manuscript and very reluctantly, he agreed to do so. My main motive for asking him to read it, was a desire for reassurance that there wasn't any material in it that would be likely to offend Bob.

He and I had what the Kray twins would have called "a little bit of an argument". My father was bitterly opposed to my deification of Bob. "Are you in love with him?" he asked furiously.

Adrian, my older brother, was also in the room.

"Yes of course she is!" he said.

Adrian and I used to bicker a lot about our respective books. We were always competing for our father's attention. My brother used to become exceptionally upset if my father didn't like a particular book which he had written. I, on the other hand, didn't care.

A frequent conversation between Adrian and myself, went along the lines of, "If you don't read my '*Koyama's Diamond*,' I won't read your "Y*our Father Had to Swing, You Little Bastard*'."

My father bullied Adrian and spoilt me. There was a lot of sibling rivalry between my brother and myself. However, I never learnt until after Adrian's death, just how devoted he was to me.

It was Adrian's mistress who had told me this.

"You've had built a bloody great gold effigy of the man, as if he were Christ!" complained my father, regarding Bob. He added, "If this book is to be a commercial venture, Rex Malone should not be recognizable as Maxwell, but should be an amalgamation of politicians, starting with Sir Winston Churchill."

"I understand what you say," I replied, "but if I leave the character, Rex Malone as he is, is there any reason why Bob would be upset by the book?"

"No, is the answer to that question. The man would be tickled pink," said my father forcefully.

I told my father I would take his advice, but did not do so.

Once I had tidied up the manuscript, I rang Ian Maxwell at his flat in the Barbican.

"I've got something very important to tell you," I said, in a tone of voice, which sounded as if all my relatives had been killed in a plane crash.

"What's up? Why all this hassle?" asked Ian.

"I have written a book, in which your father is the main character. I've made him out to be a national hero, and I've described his relationship with a sex-crazed, thuggish funeral director in some depth."

"Is the relationship sexual?" asked Ian cautiously.

"No."

"This man in your book, is he recognizable as Bob?"

(I was intrigued by the fact that he did not say "my father".)

"Yes," I said. I added, "I feel that your father should see the manuscript, before I send it to a publisher."

"I don't understand why you sound so worried. I'm going to Headington this weekend. Why don't you bring the manuscript round to my address, or send it by courier? Then I'll give it to Dad. What are you calling him?" asked Ian.

"Rex Malone."

"Jesus!"

I sent the manuscript to Ian by courier, having rubbed some of its pages with heather, sold to me by a gypsy. (I am extremely superstitious.)

My fear that Bob would consider the book too macabre, black-humoured and ribald increased. I spent Saturday and Sunday, watching horror films and drinking gin and tonic.

Ian rang me early on Monday morning. I was just about to leave for the office. I was working at the Royal Free Hospital for Dr Jean Ginsburg, a consultant endocrinologist.

"Is it all right, Ian?" I asked urgently.

"Cool it, will you! Of course, it's all right. I gave your

manuscript to Dad to read, and I also read aloud to him the passages which I thought he'd missed."

"What did he say?" I asked.

"He was very flattered and amused. He wants you to go to Headington next Saturday. Are you free then?"

"Yes. What time on Saturday?"

"Twelve noon. We're having some of Anne's friends to lunch. Dad said you can stay for dinner, and also the night, if you want. My mother's quite happy about this as well."

The following Saturday, I put on a turquoise shirt and matching turquoise trousers. I tucked the trousers into the red snakeskin, stiletto-heeled boots, which Bob had once expressed a liking for.

I was late starting, so I drove (this time a silver Ford Fiesta) at speeds of 110 miles per hour down the M40. I was getting nervous.

I arrived at Headington and stopped at a pub where I knocked back two double gin and tonics.

I drove on until I reached the outside of Headington Hill Hall. I drove past the sentry, over all the ramps, and on reaching the house, got out of the car and rang the bell.

Genius opened the door.

"Hullo," I said, "How are you keeping?"

"Very well, thank you, Miss. Mr Maxwell is waiting for you on the lawn."

I started to get very hot and agitated, despite the gin. I thought briefly about the ribaldry, morbidity, necrophilia and other negative subjects in the book, despite the fact that it portrayed Bob as a god-like figure. I panicked, rushed upstairs and took a cold bath in Bob's majestic bathroom. I feared that the gin would affect my breath. I looked around and found an almost unused tube of toothpaste. The toothpaste was strange-looking and stripey. I think it was called "Signal" or some such name.

I squeezed the contents of the tube liberally into my mouth, gargled and rinsed out. I repeated the procedure over and over again, until the tube was nearly empty.

It was more likely than not, that the toothpaste belonged to Bob. However, he would never, for a moment, have noticed that over half of it had been used, and, even more unbelievably, he would never have suspected that I had used it, to get rid of the smell of gin on my breath.

The window in the bathroom was wide open. I heard Bob speaking to Genius. His voice was loud and deep as it always was.

"Genius!"

"Yes, sir."

"Where is Eleanor Berry?"

"She went upstairs to have a bath, sir."

"Why?"

"I don't know, sir."

"What the hell do you mean, you don't know?"

I got dressed, applied a modest amount of make-up, went downstairs and out onto the lawn.

I found Bob at a table, accompanied by Jean, Ghislaine, Betty and a really weird, heavily-sweating man in black, who had been trying to talk to Bob about prayer books. It was clear that Bob was not interested in the man's conversation.

I approached Bob from behind and put my hand on his shoulder.

"Bob?" I ventured.

"There you are! Genius said you'd gone upstairs to have a bath. Why did you do that?"

"Oh, my hands were covered with oil. I had to scrub them."

"I see."

"Er… Bob?"

"Yes, Eleanor?"

"Er… Have you read my book?"

"I have."

I took a deep breath.

"What did you think of it?"

There was a pause. Bob re-lit his cigar which had just gone out. I tried to prevent myself from hyperventilating.

"I was absolutely flabbergasted by it," he replied.

"Does that mean you are giving me permission to get it published?"

"Of course, I give you permission. Go ahead and get it published. Who's publishing it?"

At that time, I had no idea who would be publishing the book. I gave the first name which came into my head.

"Weidenfeld."

Ian walked past the table, wearing a colourful bathing suit. "You can't go wrong with George," he said and dived into the swimming pool.

George Weidenfeld, (later Lord Weidenfeld) was said to be the most disreputable publisher in London by some. I think he had an affair with my mother, but I am not sure.

Bob started to quarrel with Ghislaine; he said her dress was indecent. She threatened to pour a bowl of strawberries over his head. Then she tried to persuade me to take her side against her father. Being a Smith, I began to stir things up. I was so relieved about the book, that I felt relaxed and started to joke around.

"My father is being such a pain today," complained Ghislaine.

"Fathers will always be fathers," I said inanely.[11*]

"That was a very silly remark," said Bob.

I ignored Bob's rebuke. I later learnt from Ian, the main reason for his father having been "flabbergasted". He had read a

---

11* My late cousin, Juliet Townsend, had once been a Lady-in-Waiting to Princess Margaret, whom my mother had despised. Princess Margaret was aware of this. "Why does your aunt hate me so much?" she said to Juliet.

"Oh, well, aunts will always be aunts, won't they, ma'am?" Juliet replied. Though nonsensical, I thought her remark was witty and spontaneous, hence my reply to Ghislaine's complaint.

passage in the book about an incident during a General Election campaign.

Malone, based on Bob, was shown picking up a dead body and slinging it over his shoulder, so that he could write his autograph for a brownie.

He was then shown throwing the body into the back of a hearse.

I waited for Bob and Ghislaine to stop quarrelling.

"I've shown my father the book," I said to Bob, "and he said I was to make Rex Malone an amalgamation of other characters, starting with Sir Winston Churchill."

"What the hell did he mean, an amalgamation?"

"Well, he said Rex Malone should not be recognizable as you."

"Don't worry about that," said Bob. "Don't take any notice of your Dad. Leave Rex Malone just as he is."

Bob and Ghislaine started to wrestle, which was a fucking bore. I turned to Betty and spoke to her about the book. She was amused by the fact that I had called her "Hortense Malone".

Suddenly, Bob stopped wrestling with Ghislaine, rose to his feet and lifted a baby out of a black pram. Kevin was the baby's father, and a woman called "Pandora" was the mother. The baby was about eighteen months old. She was a little girl, called "Tilly".

Bob caressed the baby girl and bounced her up and down on his knee. "She's a bundle of fun," he exclaimed. "That's what she is, a bundle of fun!" He continued to bounce her up and down.

Eventually, he put her back in her pram and left the table to have his afternoon rest.

I waited for him to come back to the lawn. I talked to some of Anne's friends and went swimming, to pass the time. Many of Anne's friends got up to leave. It was still early afternoon.

Bob came out onto the lawn at about six o'clock. He was wearing a white bath towel dressing-gown once more. I said "goodbye" to Betty and then to her husband. Anne said "goodbye" to her mother, but, strangely, she ignored her father completely. She went out into the drive, got into her car and left.

"Goodbye, Missy and good luck with your buck," said Bob to me. "Was this a Freudian slip?" I asked myself. He added, "Remember: Don't take any notice of your Dad. Keep Rex Malone the same."

I dined with my father that evening. I told him I had had lunch with Bob, who had forbidden me to tamper with Rex Malone's character. At first, I thought I was smoothing things over skilfully.

My father was quite cross, however. "You've never written a book with me as the central character," he complained. After dinner, my sister, Harriet said that my father was jealous of my affection for Bob, particularly as Bob was a newspaper magnate whereas my father had sold his papers to the thoroughly reprobate Conrad Black who ended up in prison! Bob had tried to prevent my father from selling his papers. My father said that 1985 was the worst year of his life, apart from 1982, when my mother had died. I felt profoundly guilty until after Bob's death. It was then that I wrote my father a letter, in which I said how sorry I was for having betrayed him, and for having caused him to be jealous of Bob.

In the letter, I said that I was far happier to have him (my father) as a father, than I would have been, had Bob been my father. I'm so glad I did this.

My father wrote me a wonderful letter. "You are wrong to think I was jealous of Bob," he began. Unfortunately, I have lost the letter.

I am relieved by the fact that I had reconciled with my father, and that he had not gone to his grave feeling unloved and betrayed.

Before I had written to him, however, my father, Harriet and I attended a performance of *King Lear* in London. I was terribly upset by the play and left the theatre in floods of tears, before it ended. I felt that I had been disloyal to my father and that I had been behaving like Goneril and Regan. The main cause of my guilt was the fact that I had obeyed Bob instead of my father, and had refused to alter Rex Malone's character.

* * *

I didn't visit the Maxwells for a considerable time. I think a whole year must have passed before I went to see them again.

When Bob came into the drawing room, he exclaimed, "Hullo, stranger, I haven't seen you for donkey's years!"

The book had come out and I sent Bob a copy. Thereafter, I continued to visit him and his family, as before. I had written a note to Bob, just inside the book, which said, "I did this because you saved my life."

* * *

I went to Headington Hill Hall on a summer's day once more. Bob's mood was by no means as jocular as it had been the last time we had had lunch on the lawn, however.

He came by helicopter, which landed on the lawn, a few feet away from the lunch table. His timing was immaculate. He arrived at 12:55. Lunch was at one o'clock.

"How do you manage to stay so pretty and to wear such lovely clothes, Eleanor?" he asked. (I was wearing a leopard skin dress.)

"Thank you, Bob. That was a very nice thing to say," I said banally.

I could tell that he was feeling depressed again that day, and that he was averse to small talk. Also, he was slightly irritated by my putting my fingers in my ears, to protect them from the roar of the helicopter.

Betty, Jean and a very strange-looking man, were seated at

the table. The man failed to stand up and introduce himself to Bob. He seemed somewhere in his late forties. On the credit side, he was wearing a collar and tie.

The pilot turned the engine off. Bob failed to sit down, while the stranger remained glued to his chair, looking at the plate of fresh salmon, peas and boiled potatoes in front of him.

"Who are you?" demanded Bob, in a hostile tone of voice.

The man didn't answer. Nor did he rise to his feet when his host was addressing him. I thought he was probably a deaf mute, either that or a complete halfwit.

Bob directed his piercing, hazel eyes at the man's face.

"Who are you?" he shouted once more. Still, the man remained silent.

Bob turned to me, "Who the hell's he?" he asked.

"Your guess is as good as mine, Bob. He's been sitting indoors in silence all morning and I couldn't get him to speak, for love nor money."

I turned to the man.

"You really *are* going to have to introduce yourself to Mr Maxwell. We all think you're being very rude. Do you speak English?" I asked the man peremptorily and laughed nervously.

Suddenly, and quite unexpectedly, the stranger uttered his name. I can't remember what it was, though. It was a French-sounding name.

"What the hell are you doing on these premises?" barked Bob, who was still standing up. The stranger failed to answer his excitable host yet again.

He was silent for a while. Eventually, he spoke, with a strong French accent: "I'm here because you asked me to come here," he said timidly.

"Is your mother tongue French?" asked Bob, his tone extremely hostile once more.

"Yes, sir."

Bob sat down and helped himself to fresh salmon, peas and new potatoes, served by Genius, who poured chilled white wine into his glass and the glasses of everyone else at the table.

"I don't remember asking you to come here," said Bob, adding, "How do you earn your keep?"

"I'm on the *Mirror*," said the man, while I struggled to keep a straight face.

Bob addressed the man in French and *tutoyed* him throughout the interview.

"What have you learnt since you started to work on the *Mirror*?" Bob's French accent sounded weird. He spoke the language with a strong, East European lilt.

The man answered his question, as best he could and bumbled on in a monotonous, sleep-inducing tone of voice. I dreaded to think what his prose must have been like, if he were continuing to write for the *Mirror*. Betty struggled to keep her eyes open. Jean yawned.

"I want to ask you a question, Bob," I called across the table.

"All right, Eleanor. What's your question?"

"It's about that book I wrote (*Never Alone with Rex Malone*). It's out of print now, but it's going to be reprinted. May I quote you as having said, you were 'absolutely flabbergasted' by it when you read it?"

"Yes," replied Bob.

"Good. May I also quote you as having said, 'I didn't know what had hit me?'"

"No."

The stranger entered the conversation at this point. This time, he spoke English, very hesitantly and with a pronounced French accent: "Mr Maxwell," he began. "I'm told that the Head of the Ethiopian Government once presented you with a silver cup, which is engraved with a statement of gratitude, for your apparent kindness and generosity towards the famine victims of Ethiopia. May I please see the cup?"

I could tell that the man was weak and gutless. He was

terrified of Bob and was trying to suck up to him. Bob loathed men like that. So do I. He only respected those who stood their ground. Whenever someone stood up to him, he respected that person. When that person was frightened and intimidated him, he invariably became hostile and treated his victim with disdain.

He put two fingers in his mouth and wolf-whistled. Genius came to the table with his hands clasped in front of him. He looked like a combination of Lurch from *The Adams Family* and the enigmatic mute lackey from *Waiting for Godot*.

"You whistled for me, Mr Maxwell," said Genius.

"Yes. There's a silver cup with an engraving on it, on the shelf in my study, next door to the drawing room. Bring it outside," said Bob impatiently.

Genius scuttled off. He took a long time to find the cup, which indicated that it was somewhere else. He came back to the table, empty-handed.

"The cup isn't where you said it was, Mr Maxwell," he ventured.

Bob looked exasperated. He rose from his chair and walked towards the house, with Genius following him meekly.

In fact, the cup was in one of the secretaries' offices. It was on a desk, next to a computer. Bob carried the cup to the table with Genius at his heels once more.

"It's all right, Genius. It wasn't your fault this time," said Bob. Genius returned to the house.

Jean took the cup from Bob's hand and offered it to the stranger, who made oily, complimentary comments about the wording of the engraving on it.

It cannot be denied that Bob had been quite rude to the stranger but, because of his failure to stick up for himself, and to say who he was in a fearless manner, Bob considered him to be a weakling. He couldn't stand weaklings. He shovelled food into his mouth and helped himself to more white wine.

There was a silence which I broke.

"I understand Ghislaine's got a business going, selling executive gifts," I said.

"You understand right," said Bob. He was definitely having an "off" day.

When he had finished eating, he wolf-whistled for Genius once more.

"Have you read a ghost story by M. R. James, entitled, '*Oh, whistle to me and I'll come to you, my lad?*'" I asked, my voice raised.

"No," replied Bob, adding, "There's no need to shout."

By this time, Genius had arrived at the table.

"You wanted to see me, Mr Maxwell," he said.

"Yes. Get the pilot out of the house and bring him here. I'm leaving," He reminded me a bit of Mr Rochester. Genius did as he was told.

Bob had only been on the lawn for about ten minutes!

The pilot came to the table. "I'm leaving now," repeated Bob, abruptly. I had hysterical giggles. The pilot helped him to get into the helicopter, after he had kissed me, "goodbye". He didn't say "goodbye" to either Betty or Jean. This, I found singular. I still couldn't stop laughing.

"Good luck with all your writing," said Bob, adding, "Be sure to come and see me in London. Incidentally, what the hell are you laughing at?"

"Oh, nothing."

The intolerably loud helicopter engine started. The next minute, it was in the sky.

"Good God," thought I, "The man's even more eccentric than I am!"

* * *

I saw Bob, once a month on average, after his short visit to Headington Hill Hall that summer's day.

One weekend, he invited me to watch a football match near

131

his house. He had bought Oxford United, a team which was playing Port Vale.

The match was due to take place on a Saturday afternoon. Bob promised me that I would be able to sit in the Director's Box, where champagne would be served.

As always, he kept his promise. About a week before the match, I wrote him a very cheeky and intimate letter in Russian, using Laurence Kelly's Cyrillic typewriter once more. I addressed Bob as "Ti", the Russian equivalent of "Tu", throughout the letter.

He replied in English:

Dear Eleanor,

Thank you for your charming Russian note. Saturday, 3 March is an away game but we will be happy to see you on the 10th, when we are playing Port Vale at home.

Yours ever, Bob

I did not realize how proverbially boring the football match would be.

I was bitterly disappointed, despite the champagne. I thought I would be able to sit next to Bob in the Director's Box, but he was sitting next to Ghislaine. There were other members of his family present.

Before the match, Bob told us all that he planned to leave prior to the end of the game. This meant that we would have had to walk about five miles, which was the distance between the football pitch and Headington Hill Hall. I was sorry I had not brought my car. I was wearing my uncomfortable, snakeskin, stiletto-heeled boots and I didn't fancy the idea of walking five miles while wearing them.

To my astonishment, Bob got up to leave about five minutes after the beginning of the match.

"I'm coming with you," I said spontaneously. I told my father about this and he said I had been unpardonably rude to Bob.

I got into the Rolls which he drove himself. There was no sign of Mr Hoppitt. The traffic between the football pitch and Headington Hill Hall was pretty bad. Neither Bob nor I spoke throughout the journey.

I got out of the Rolls and closed the door very gently, when we had reached our destination.

"No," said Bob.

"No?"

"You haven't closed the door properly. Try again."

He didn't comment about my ungracious behaviour. "I'm going upstairs for a rest," he said abruptly.

I sat in the drawing room, until he came down from his rest. Betty was there and she and I had a long conversation about Bob's deterioration in mood and general health.

I had noticed that he was not looking his usual self. Betty commented that he had recently recovered from a winter virus which had affected his appearance.

His face was sterner that it had been in the past. There had not been much increase in his weight, however, although Betty said that there had been a decline in his behaviour towards others.

She told me that he had been increasingly intolerant of fools, and that he had become more short-tempered towards her, than he had been in the past.

He came down from his rest at about six o'clock. He did not say a word to me about my having insisted on leaving the football match five minutes after the game had started. He was extremely friendly towards me and asked me to visit him in London once more. Even so, I thought he looked sad and ill. I hoped with all my heart that there was nothing seriously wrong with him.

Once I arrived in London, I watched a nauseating television programme entitled, *Some Mothers do 'ave 'em*. Whoever the star of the programme was, he caused me to be phenomenally depressed and irritated. I wondered what Bob would have thought about this man. Not much, I concluded.

* * *

In June, 1988, Bob celebrated his sixty-fifth birthday. He gave three parties, all of which were at Headington Hill Hall. One was on 10th June, which was his actual birthday; another was on 11th June and yet another was on 12th June.

The party on 11th June appeared to me to be the most attractive, since it was due to take place at lunch time. I had not received an invitation, so I just turned up. I knew Bob used to do that himself, and I was sure he would be pleased to see me, with or without an invitation. Incidentally, this was something I did every single June.

It was a cold day for the time of year, so I wore tight-fitting, white leather trousers, a white V-necked sweater, and my red snakeskin boots over the trousers. I had on matching red earrings and jewellery. I had had my hair done and had had a facial and a manicure the day before.

The sentry stopped me at the gate, leading to Headington Hill Hall. I lowered the window and leant out of the car.

"Hullo, there. Long time no see. My name is Eleanor Berry and I've lost my invitation card, blast it! How are you keeping?"

The sentry pressed a button and opened the gate.

The lawn was covered with a marquee. I went inside and saw a buffet and tables, at which guests, whose faces I did not recognize, guzzled.

A cinema screen showed a film about Bob and his achievements. I became elated and helped myself to a drink.

Later, I found Jean. A *Mirror* photographer took a picture of her and me standing together.

"Have you seen Bob recently?" I asked her.

"Not recently. He's been moving all over the place."

I walked about, went to a table and asked some of the guests questions.

"He came through here ten minutes ago," said a woman.

"Where did he go after that?" I asked. The unnecessarily alarmed expression on her face was similar to what I had imagined the wedding guest's would have been, when he had been button-holed by the Ancient Mariner.

"I think he went indoors," said the woman vaguely.

"Where exactly? Can you take me to him?"

"I can't. I've never met the man," said the woman. I thought she was a brick short of a load.

"Do you really mean you don't know him?"

"No, I've never met him in my life."

"What are you doing here, then?"

"He took my name from the telephone directory, I suppose," said the woman.

"Oh, bollocks!" I said.

I moved to another table and questioned its occupants in a similar manner. Then I saw one of Bob's twin daughters, leading a tiny child by the hand.

"Christine!" I called out.

"It's not Christine. It's Isabel."

"Oh, sorry. Do you know where your father is?"

"He's somewhere on the lawn, I think. By the way, I liked some parts of your *Never Alone with Rex Malone* but not all of it. It was very disturbing and macabre in places. You treated my parents interestingly and kindly, though, and I thank you for that," said Isabel.

"I know. I read your letter." I said, "Come on, Isabel, the book wasn't that macabre. Let's go and find your father."

"I'm going to see him myself. Why don't you come with me?"

I couldn't keep up with Isabel, because my stiletto heels kept getting stuck in the mud. She waited for me. Then she led me to her father.

Her small son, Alexander, had painted a picture on the cover of a book. It was a birthday present for Bob who was standing in an inner area. I didn't know which room he was in, because the ceiling and walls were draped with white cloth, like an Arab's tent.

"Hullo, Bob. Happy birthday," I said. I handed him a wrapped-up jar of caviar. I put my hands on both his shoulders and kissed him on each cheek.

"May I open my present now?" he said charmingly.

"Yes," I said.

He was looking much healthier and happier than he had looked on the day of the football match. As always, he was very pleased to see me. He introduced me to some men who were roughly the same age as he.

"This is Eleanor Berry and I'm one of her greatest admirers," he began. "When she was in her teens, she joined the Communist Party and went to Russia alone, having taught herself to speak Russian like a native. She's got guts, all right." He added, "Eleanor's got a hell of a lot of stories to tell you all about her adventures. She got a job as a nanny once but she only lasted for ten minutes!"

There was muffled laughter. Bob turned to Isabel's son who handed him the picture book. Its cover was worded in a childlike hand; he had probably been helped by an adult,

"*To Grandad who lives in a helicopter all day.*"

Bob laughed and picked the boy up. Isabel helped herself to crudités and passed the dish to me.

"Why did your nanny job only last for ten minutes?" she asked.

"I'm at a loss to understand," I replied, adding, "I turned up at the house and found the children's mother in the kitchen. I introduced myself. Then I asked her to call her children into the kitchen.

"She called them and gave me a rather curious look. Three

136

strapping teenaged boys, who didn't need a nanny, came into the kitchen. 'Would you please stand against the wall, in order of size, and give me your names,' I said. I had remembered one of the early scenes in the film, *The Sound of Music*. The boys gave me their names.

"'Bring your ball outside onto the lawn, so that I can have a game with you and get to know you better.' I said.

"'Your services are no longer required,' said their mother, as if I had actually assaulted the boys.

"'Why are my services no longer required? You haven't sampled them yet,' I said.

"'I would like you to leave my house now,' the mother replied.

"'I'll do just that, madam. Anyway, your sons are far too big to need a nanny, unless they are mentally retarded. Maybe they are.'"

Isabel laughed. "Ellie, you're quite mad!" she said.

Bob laughed as well. He spoke to me in Russian, and it was fortunate that I had been brushing up my Russian, for a good six weeks before his birthday.

We had a short conversation in Russian and I said I could only speak the language perfectly, if I was drunk. (I said this is Russian.)

Bob roared with laughter and I laughed with him. None of the other people present, including Isabel and her son, spoke Russian. Speaking Russian seemed to strengthen my bond with Bob.

I was determined to sit next to him at lunch and went into the kitchen, where I found Betty. I greeted her and helped her into her pale green Dior jacket, which accentuated her auburn hair. Lunch consisted of lobster, liver pâté, caviar, cheese and strawberries with cream. I was sitting opposite Bob.

He poured some vodka into his glass to drink with the caviar.

"May I have some vodka, please, Bob," I asked.

"No. It will make you ill. The last time you got drunk here,

137

you started talking to me about mortuaries and necrophilia!"[12*]

I struggled to keep a straight face. "Oh, please, Bob. Go on, be a sport."

"No, I categorically forbid it!"

He then addressed everyone at the table, collectively and spoke about his experiences during the War. I desperately tried to catch his eye but failed.

I had brought my happy pills with me. I had taken some of these earlier but they were beginning to wear off. I threw my napkin under the table, to give the impression that I had dropped it, got under the table and took another dose of happy pills, which I chewed up.

When I got up, I noticed a youngish woman, sitting on Bob's right side. She was slim, had long, dishevelled blonde hair and was wearing a transparent braless, black top, which left nothing to the imagination.

Her short skirt was strategically raised, and one of her legs was bent and could be seen above the table. She was speaking to Bob in some Eastern European language. She was deliberately leaving me out of the conversation, and was trying to get as much of his attention as she could.

I wasn't going to tolerate any of this, and I fixed her with a homicidal stare. I'm sure Betty also resented her presence and her brazen behaviour.

I caught her eye. "Stop monopolizing Bob, or you'll be sorry," I said. I added, "He's a married man. This is a respectable place, not a disorderly house." Bob didn't hear a word I said.

He was called to the phone. Some Head of State or other was wishing him a happy birthday. When he returned to the table, the Eastern European woman continued to try to chat him up, but I constantly interrupted her. Besides, my happy pills were

---

[12*] This is a reference to an unfortunate story which I had once told Bob when I was intoxicated.

beginning to kick in, which enabled me to be much bolder than I had been earlier.

"Bob!"

"Yes, Eleanor. Why are you shouting?"

"Shouting?"

"Yes, you're shouting, as if I were outside in the bloody street!"

I was undeterred. I was so high on the happy pills that I was hitting Jupiter. "I want to ask you a question," I said.

"Well, what's your question?"

"May I please have a signed copy of Joe Haines's biography of you? It could be a late birthday present."

"When was your birthday?"

"A month ago."

"What date?"

"May 6th."

Bob then continued to tell his listeners about his experiences during the War. Apart from Betty, the blonde hussy and myself, the people at the table were total strangers. Their names had indeed been taken out of the telephone directory. Nicky was right.

Bob left the table and went indoors for his afternoon rest.

The East European woman looked dejected. I went up to her and beckoned her away from the table, onto the lawn, as I knew she intended to wait for Bob to come down after his rest.

She came onto the lawn with me. She was drunk. I roughed her about a bit. Her balance was poor and she fell over. I knelt down beside her. The happy pills continued to give me courage. I said, "Mrs Maxwell is extremely distressed by the lewd advances which you have been making towards her husband. She has told me that she would like you to leave the premises."

I added, "In England, it is a serious criminal offence to seduce someone's husband. The offence is punishable by a stiff jail sentence, and conditions in British jails are very unpleasant. In fact, Mr Maxwell was so embarrassed by your amorous advances towards him that he was obliged to leave the table and go indoors."

Somehow, I managed to keep a straight face. The woman was not very bright. She left, having believed every word I uttered.

Within a week, I received Joe Haines's book. Bob had even remembered when my birthday was. He had written, "To Eleanor, from Bob, in friendship." I have always kept the book. I had just returned from a friend's funeral when it reached me. It cheered me up for the rest of the day.

* * *

I stayed at Headington Hill Hall at a later date but Bob wasn't there. It was a Friday.

I got out of my car and carried my suitcase, together with a bouquet of flowers, to the front door which Genius opened.

"Good evening. Is Mr Maxwell at home?" I asked.

"No, Miss."

"Do you know whether he will be coming home tomorrow?"

"I don't know."

"Is he ill?"

"I don't know anything about him, Miss."

"Oh? I thought you worked for him."

"Sometimes, I do. Sometimes, I don't."

"Where is he?"

"He could be anywhere, Miss". Then I understood that this man wasn't called "Genius" for nothing.

"Mrs Maxwell's here, Miss. May I take your suitcase?" said Genius.

"Thank you."

The first thing I needed was a stiff gin and tonic. I went to the drinks cabinet in the drawing room and helped myself. Bob's nephew was in the room. He was the son of Sylvia Rosen, Bob's sister. (Bob's two sisters were the only members of the Hoch family, who had survived the Holocaust. Their names were Sylvia and Brana.)

Sylvia's son, whose name I can't remember, was almost eight foot tall, which was why Bob sometimes referred to him ironically as the "dwarf". He had a nickname for many of the people he knew or knew of.

He referred to Oping, his cook, as "Opium". He referred to my paternal aunt, Sheila Birkenhead, as "the old Banbury aunt", because she lived near Banbury. I could give endless examples of Bob's child-like sense of humour.

"Where's your uncle?" I asked the "dwarf".

"I haven't the faintest idea where he is. I saw Ghislaine yesterday. She had a cold."

I regarded this as unsolicited information. I went over to the drinks cabinet and poured myself another gin and tonic. Within a few minutes, I felt easier.

Eventually, Betty came downstairs. I greeted her and gave her the flowers I had brought with me.

"Is Bob not well?" I asked.

"He's not at all well. I'm afraid he's had to stay at the *Mirror*. He's got bad toothache and I'm trying to get hold of a dentist."

"I'm sorry to hear that! Am I allowed to smoke a cigarette in here?" I asked.

"*Mais non!*" said Betty emphatically.

"I know a good dentist called 'Russell King' at 29 Cavendish Square, in London." I wrote his name and phone number down on a piece of paper. "I'm not sure whether he practices at weekends, though," I said.

"Oh dear!"

"What about ringing *Yellow Pages*? If you do that, you will be able to find a list of dentists and information about whether they work at weekends. I'll ring them, one by one, if you like."

"That's very sweet of you, Eléanore. At the moment, I could do with a drink. What will you have?"

The gin was getting to my head. I was feeling uneasy on my feet.

Perrier and ice, please," I said.

"I can see you live dangerously! Won't you have something stronger?"

"I won't, thank you."

Genius came into the drawing room to say that dinner was ready.

"Are you writing another book?" asked Betty at dinner.

"Not yet, I'm afraid. I've been in deadlock for eighteen months, blast it!"

"Oh, you lazy old thing!"

"I continued to speak to Betty. The "dwarf" was subdued and failed to contribute towards the conversation. After dinner, Betty took me to her study and showed me some leather-bound albums. These contained press cuttings about her husband. They went back to the days when publicity about Bob had first started to take place.

She also showed me many of Bob's letters, written when he was wooing her. Although his handwriting was appalling, I could just about decipher his words.

We stayed up until one o'clock in the morning, when Betty must have been exhausted. She showed me to my room. I took a bath, cleaned my teeth, got into bed and read Edgar Allan Poe's poem *Ulalume*, my favourite of all his poems.

I went down to breakfast at eight thirty the following morning. Betty came down at about nine o'clock. We were eating in the kitchen. I rose to my feet and greeted her. She addressed me in French, but my French was particularly rusty that day, because I hadn't slept too well the night before. I also had a terrible hangover.

"Will you let me ring up Russell King, the dentist?" I began (in English). "Perhaps I could ring some other dentists up as well, if he's not available on a Saturday."

"How kind of you to ask me! I've already managed to contact a dental practice who are available for 24 hours a day. Bob's seeing a dentist at eleven o'clock."

"Ah, yes."

Genius brought me some fresh orange juice and toast. He gave Betty a pile of newspapers, among which was *The Guardian*. There was no *Daily Telegraph* among them. Later on, I helped her to put a colossal pile of Christmas cards into envelopes. They appeared to be addressed to each citizen of every country in the world. My father and I were included. (My mother was already dead.)

This year's card was fairly low profile. It showed the words, "Pergamon Press", in gold letters against a frosty, blue background.

Whenever I stayed with the Maxwells, just before Christmas, I took my father's and my card away with me. I learnt something through many disagreeable experiences. Every Christmas, guests came to our house in Buckinghamshire. If Bob's photograph appeared on his and Betty's card, particularly if his photograph was unflattering, foul-mannered guests would take the card down from the mantelpiece and pass it round the room.

A regular culprit of this offence was one of Lord Longford's many sons. I can't name him because of the bloody libel laws, although I would like to. This man has the manners of a concentration camp lavatory attendant, and a tendency to dominate conversations, as well as to interrupt people all the time and change the subject.

Someone had informed me that he had once been the British Ambassador in some Third World country. An ambassador?!! Stone the bloody crows, thought I. He has a very likeable wife, though. Few people like her, but I do. Another culprit was called Anthea Lambert-Perry (name changed). She is the wife of a very able barrister. He was a once brilliant but has gone into decline.

"Why does that man have to put his photograph on his Christmas cards?" she asked in a shrill tone of voice. Also, like

Lord Longford's odious son, she was insulting my father in his own home, which was unforgivable. Both had actually taken the cards from the mantlepiece.

I put my mouth to her ear.

"*What* did you say?" I shouted.

Fear came into her voice and onto her face. She was pretty gutless.

"I only asked why that man had to put his photograph on his Christmas cards," she muttered, very timidly.

"I'll tell you why!" I shouted, "Because the person you so rudely refer to as 'that man' committed nothing other than heroic acts during the War, in the interests of the freedom which you now enjoy. Also, the person you refer to as 'that man' saved my fucking life! If you had done so much as a quarter of the things he had done, I bet *you* would have sent out photographs of yourself at Christmas!"

The woman got up and went to another part of the room. I noticed she had wet the cushion she had been sitting on.

My father was always very loyal towards me and was really sporting about the Maxwells' cards. The next time Lord Longford's jumped-up brat criticized one of the Maxwells' cards, my father flew into a rage.

"How dare you come to my house and make unacceptably rude remarks about the Christmas cards sent to me by my friends!"

I kissed my father on the forehead.

"Oh, thank you, Daddy!" I said.

I was taught a lesson. Every time I went to the Maxwells' house, just before Christmas, I destroyed their card addressed to my father.

"I haven't heard from Uncle Bob this year," he commented.

"Oh, Betty said she wouldn't be sending any more Christmas cards in future. She said she had been under too much pressure of late," I lied.

I can't tell you how much I hate Lord Longford's brat! Not

only did I say that he had the manners of a concentration camp lavatory attendant. I can prove this, with further evidence.

Once, when my father was in the South of France, Lord Longford's brat visited his house in Buckinghamshire. It was locked up. He wanted to watch *Match of the Day* so he tried to break a window, to enable him to get into the house. Fortunately, he failed to do so.

Why couldn't he have watched *Match of the Day*, in his own house? Didn't he possess a television?

On another occasion, when my mother was alive, he came to stay in our house, when he had gastric flu. He stayed with us for over a week, and sometimes he failed to make it to the bathroom. My mother used to call him the "bilious boy." Incidentally, he gave us all his germs.

Why could he not have stayed at home if he was ill? Not only that, he didn't even write a thank-you letter to my parents afterwards.

Another thing I despise about him is his voice. It's simpering, drone-like and effeminate. He is not interested in other people's opinions, lives or feelings. All he thinks and talks about is himself.

The thing I loathe most about him is that he frequently made a mockery of Bob, and had also insulted my father in his own home, like the barrister's wife who couldn't hold her water.

* * *

SOME TIME LATER

I rang Bob's office at the *Mirror* and invited myself for a drink with him. He had often asked me to make a date to see him. I decided to take him up on his offer.

Annabella Williams (name changed), Bob's personal secretary, by whom he was absolutely besotted, took my call. I had seen a photograph of him and her walking barefoot, on a beach, towards the sea. I was jealous.

"What do you want to talk to Mr Maxwell about?" asked Annabella officiously.

"I'm sure Mr Maxwell will tell you, if he thinks you need to know," I replied. I continued, "Would you please look for a free evening in his diary, without asking me any more silly questions."

Annabella became more genial. She named a date. "He's free then but only for a drink. Last time you rang, you said you wanted to be shown round the *Mirror*. Mr Maxwell would love to show you round the *Mirror* but he has to go out afterwards, as I said."

"That sounds fine," I said.

"Mrs Maxwell will be coming to the *Mirror* that evening, so you'll be able to see her too."

* * *

I slept badly the night before I was due to go to the *Mirror*. I bought Bob some caviar and a bouquet of flowers for Betty. At that time, I was working as a medical secretary at Barts (St Bartholomew's Hospital).

I had been given two lengthy "discharge summaries" to type. I told my boss that I would be unable to type them that day. I said I had a migraine.

I hailed a taxi and told the driver to leave me near the *Mirror*. I found a pub, had a double gin and tonic and buried myself in a novel by James Hadley Chase.

I had another double gin and tonic, because I was afraid of going into the *Mirror* building and not being able to find Bob there.

The smell of gin must have been on my breath but I hadn't consumed enough for my speech to be affected. I swallowed two or three happy pills, waited for them to kick in, and went into the *Mirror* building.

"I'm here to see Mr Maxwell," I said to a man behind a desk, on the ground floor, adding, "He is expecting me. My name is Eleanor Berry."

The man rang Bob's office and showed me to the lift. I had noticed in passing that the ground floor looked clean but very ordinary. The lift went up to the top floor. When the doors opened, I saw an entirely new world.

I am not an authority on interior decoration, but the room, which the lift had brought me to looked majestic and was adorned with seventeenth and eighteenth century paintings.

The furniture was Empire, like that in the drawing room at Headington Hill Hall. The carpets were embroidered with a single letter M on them. There was no-one there to greet me, however. A window, which covered an entire wall, showed a panoramic view of London.

I became restless and walked round in circles. I noticed a chess set, comprised of intricately carved pieces. A game was in progress. I moved the pieces back to their original places and started a game with myself. I walked backwards and forwards, whistling, "*A Silent Crowd Gathered Outside of Kilmainham*", a well-known Irish rebel song.

A bossy employee of Bob's suddenly came into the room. He was brown-haired, clean-shaven and nondescript.

"You shouldn't have moved those men," he said in an anxious tone of voice. "You have interrupted a game between Mr Maxwell and the Russian Ambassador."

"Dearie me!"

"I really would thank you not to touch his men in future. He's very proud of them," continued the man.

"I won't touch them again. Scout's honour."

"Would you like something to drink?"

"Yes, please, a gin and tonic. Where is Mr Maxwell?"

"He's still in his office. He knows you're here. He'll be with you shortly."

Within about half an hour, Betty came into the room, splendidly dressed. She told me she was going out to dinner. I handed her the flowers I had brought.

She and I had a long conversation about the lives of her children, who were, on the whole, doing well and were reasonably happy. She talked at length about her husband. She said he was working too hard and that she was worried about his health.

"With Bob, work is play," I said, "When he works, he is like a child playing with his toys. I think this does him a lot of good. If he stopped working, he'd go off his head."

"I hope you're right." Betty changed the subject. "Ghislaine bought an evening dress in Paris last week." Betty described the dress at length. I switched off.

"You *are* all right, aren't you?" she asked suddenly. I may have appeared fidgety and uncoordinated, due to the happy pills and the gin.

"Yes, I am all right," I said, adding, "Has Ghislaine got another boyfriend? Oh, sorry, that's none of my business."

"She's been going out with the same man for some time now," replied Betty. She gave me his name, which was so lengthy, that it would have covered the front page of a tabloid newspaper.

"Does Bob like him?" I asked.

"No. That's where there's a problem. He can't stand him."

"Why not?"

"There are two reasons why not," said Betty. "One is that Bob is intensely jealous of him. The other is that the young man is Italian and he can't abide Italians. He thinks they're all drunken idiots."

I laughed. I have always found jealousy in a man attractive. We talked for a few more minutes, until Betty had to leave. We said "goodbye" and she walked towards the lift. The nondescript man came back into the room. He said he had complained to Bob about the chess pieces, but his boss never mentioned this to me.

"You won't have to wait much longer, Miss Berry. Mr Maxwell will be ready to see you as soon as he has finished his phone call."

I still smoked in those days and I knew the consequences of smoking in front of Bob. He abhorred smokers because of the lung operation he had had when he was younger. (I have spoken about this before.) A receptionist ushered me into a lavish hallway, with magenta, velvet chairs, where she said I could smoke, provided I put my cigarette out, as soon as Bob came out of his office. I didn't want him to see me smoking, so I had a cigarette in his private lavatory. The dreaded Annabella Williams, Bob's adored secretary, was standing outside the lavatory.

"You had a cigarette in Mr Maxwell's lavatory," she said confrontationally. "Mr Maxwell *knows* you had a cigarette in his lavatory."

I couldn't understand what Bob saw in her. She was plain and was wearing a ridiculously short miniskirt, which left nothing to the imagination. In fact, it was so bloody short, that it was just about possible to see her cervix.

"What were you really doing in Mr Maxwell's lavatory?" asked Annabella.

The happy pills continued to have a wonderful effect on me.

"You are a shorthand typist and I am a distinguished woman of letters. When I die, my profile will be engraved on the coins. When your time comes up, no-one will know or care that you'd ever existed."

I can't tell you how jealous I was of this woman.

I also noticed her thick, green eye shadow. I thought it was awfully naff.

"Do you have psychiatric problems, Miss Berry?" she asked rudely.

"Oh, piss off, you silly little nit!" I said, my voice raised.

Bob never mentioned this *contretemps* to me. That is what

was so nice about him. I think, secretly, he was turned on by Annabella's any my argument, if you can call it that.

The happy pills were making my heart race. There were quite a few boring-looking women outside Bob's office, all of whom were dressed in boring-looking uniforms. They were his other secretaries. I asked one of them to give me a copy of the *Mirror*. I started to do the crossword.

Within about ten minutes, Bob came to the door of his office and beckoned me in. He kissed me on both cheeks and said how pleased he was to see me. I noticed that he had the blinds drawn and the lights turned off, except for an Anglepoise lamp on his desk. Also, his office was strangely very small, unlike the office he occupied previously.

"You're looking more beautiful by the minute," he said. I stared at him flirtatiously.

"Thank you, Bob. I've brought you some *Beluga*." I know you like it.

"Oh, thank you, Pussycat! May I open my present now?" He always said that when I gave him a present. He sounded childlike, like the vulnerable Czech boy who had had neither enough clothes nor enough to eat when he was little.

"Yes, of course," I said. "I hope it's the one you like. I can change it if it isn't."

Bob changed the subject.

"There's something worrying you, isn't there, Pussycat?" he said suddenly. "Come on. Let's have it. You can tell Bob." How I loved him then!

At that time, I was very preoccupied with the woman I shared an office with. I was a permanent medical secretary but she was only a temp. This meant that she had no rights to speak of. She was a luckless policeman's wife. I will refer to her as "Stinker".

I knew Stinker would be trouble from the moment she entered my office. It was her first day of employment at St Bartholomew's Hospital, where I had worked hard for five years. She was tall, had long, dishevelled, reddish hair and wore black-rimmed glasses. She looked like the Witch of Endor.

She spoke with a pronounced lisp. "There'th one word I don't ever want to hear uttered in thith offith, and that'th a word that beginnth with an F," she said.

"You'll hear what I fucking well want you to hear!" I replied.

It was raining hard. She had carried an umbrella into the office and had opened it up. I refused to tolerate this because I am very superstitious. It is known to be unlucky to open an umbrella indoors.

"Close that fucking umbrella!" I commanded. "It's bad luck to have an umbrella open indoors."

She refused to close the umbrella. We were working in a small office and its spikes were getting in the way of the piles of casenotes on the floor. I got up, closed the umbrella and threw it out of the office into the corridor.

Stinker was disgustingly genteel and sniffed all the time. She had a grating, high-pitched voice and her opinions about current affairs were to the Right of centre, although she knew nothing about politics.

She commented adversely about the one and a half hour lunch breaks which I took every day. I wanted to be out of the office for as long as possible.

"You're only supposed to take one hour for lunch. My taxes pay for the extra half hour that you take on a habitual basis," said Stinker. She had only been employed at Barts for three weeks at this time!

"I beg your pardon?"

"You heard me."

"I'm sorry. I don't think I did." I said.

I kept a series of flick-knives in my top drawer. At that time, I collected flick-knives, which I had been smuggling into Heathrow from Marseille. I had thirty-two of them. I loved the way they went *click-huitt, click-huitt*, on being opened and closed.

I didn't trust Stinker to bring the doctors' mail to the office, so I opened all the letters myself, with one of my flick-knives. There were three consultant physicians on the firm. They were Dr William Ross Cattell (an absolute dear), Professor Anthony Raine and lastly a doctor whom I will refer to as Dr "Beria". Dr Beria was the most senior of all the doctors.

Stinker was shocked when I got out my flick-knife. "My husband, who, as you know, is a policeman, says it's illegal to carry a flick-knife," she commented with her nauseating lisp. She pronounced the word "policeman" as "pliceman".

"I'm not interested in what your fucking husband says!" I replied.

"I can't bear your disgusting language," she said.

"Don't lecture me about the English language. I hold a BA Hons degree in it!"

I knew that in the interests of my sanity, I would have to get rid of Stinker. I was friendly with most of the medical secretaries in other departments. Few of these women could bear her, either. At about eleven o'clock every morning, we had tea in the canteen. Whenever Stinker came into the room, we all got up and walked out.

The other women were unable to tolerate the effect she was having on me. They, too, wanted her to leave.

"It seems as if I'm universally disliked," said Stinker mildly, when we met again in the office.

"That's fucking fair comment," I replied, "Can't you see you're not wanted?"

Despite my increasingly hostile behaviour towards her, and my frequent use of the F word, Stinker still wouldn't leave. She was like Edgar Allan Poe's *Raven*. I tried another tack. I bought some cloves of garlic, put them into my mouth and chewed them up. Although I hate garlic, I felt I had to do this, to prevent me from cracking up.

As a result, our office reeked of garlic. Stinker loathed the smell; this was a promising sign.

I was working at my computer one morning, and she sprayed a strong-smelling deodorant round my head. I snatched it from her hand, threw it out of the window and continued to work at my computer.

I found out something about Stinker's married life, from one of the other medical secretaries. Apparently, she talked about me non-stop during breakfast, dinner and even during the sex act. Her husband, the policeman, could stand it no longer.

"If I hear one more word from you about Eleanor bloody Berry, I'm going to divorce you, and I really do mean that!" he shouted, one night, during the sex act once more.

The day before I was due to meet Bob at the *Mirror*, I had been told that Stinker was thinking of becoming "permanent". This would have deprived me of all my rights, and would have made my life so unbearable that it would have been necessary for me to resign.

I told Bob about the problems I had been having with Stinker, but not at inordinate length, because he preferred verbal conciseness.

Incidentally, I got the name "Stinker" from my father. He and my mother lived next door to Sir John Gielgud (the actor). He was a blithering nuisance. He owned a noisy parrot which he kept in his garden and which recited, "*To Be or Not to Be*" at two o'clock in the morning onwards.

When I was two months old, my mother wheeled me in my pram up to the fence, dividing Sir John Gielgud's' house from that of my parents. Predictably, at that age, I made a hell of a lot of noise, and prevented the recalcitrant actor from being able to learn his lines. He called the police.

"Don't day-dream, Pussycat. What's worrying you?" said Bob.

I used concise language, but told Bob everything I thought he needed to know about Stinker.

He sat at his desk with his hand supporting his chin, and his hazel eyes permanently wandering.

I also told him that Stinker had been thinking of becoming permanent, thus depriving me of all my rights.

"Blimey, Missy, you need to get rid of Stinker, as soon as you possibly can," said Bob emphatically.

I knew he was interested in my problem, but I overdid things a bit. It was the gin and happy pills speaking.

"Stinker takes *The Sun*",[13*] I lied, "and she encourages all the other medical secretaries to do the same."

"Why?" came the terse response. This time, it was Maxwell speaking, rather than the poor Czech boy.

"Well, she just does," I eventually managed to mutter.

There was a silence. Bob chewed his unlit cigar. "Why don't you give up all this medical secretarial work, and work for me at the *Mirror* instead?" he asked, adding, "When I offered you a job some years ago, you turned me down. Perhaps, this time, you'll say 'yes'."

"How can I give up my job, Bob? I adore it. I like the hustle and bustle of be-stethoscoped, white-coated doctors, running down corridors, the to-ing and fro-ing of stretchers borne by sweating porters, and the toiling of blood-splattered, green-clad surgeons, cutting up bodies. I also like watching operations and attending post-mortems."

I wouldn't have said all this, had I not been drinking and taking the happy pills, even though the latter were becoming less affective.

"Missy, you're bloody barmy!" exclaimed Bob. "So you're saying, in so many words, that you like the stench of death and decay. You can't fool me. I've known you since you were a puppy. You've

---

13* One of the *Mirror's* rival papers. Sometimes, at about eleven o'clock at night, I drove to Bouverie Street where the presses of *The Sun* and *The News of the World* used to be. I threw objects into the presses, in the hope that the papers would come out with a blank front page.

I also bought a handful of nails and threw them out of my car, on the driver's side. I threw them in front of the lorries, delivering the News of the World's first editions.

I told Ian I had been doing this but he told me to stop, on the grounds that my activities might cause his father bad publicity.

always been potty about blood and guts. You used to go to people's funerals, because they turned you on. That's what made you like Russian literature. It is moribund. You told me that yourself."

"When?" I asked. I was rather embarrassed.

"In the campaign van, going to Oxford from Buckingham, just after I'd lost my seat in the 1970 General Election.

"I don't remember discussing these matters with you Bob," I said, "I only remember talking to you about the novel, *Foma Gordyev* by Gorki."

"I've got a much better memory than you have Pussycat," said Bob.

There was a silence. Then I said, "I inherit my passion for the macabre from my maternal grandmother. It's not my fault. It's the gene. She even attended the trial of Crippen when pieces of his wife's dead body were passed round."

Bob changed the subject. "How much do they pay you at St Bartholomew's Hospital?" he asked.

I named a sum which was twice the amount of what I actually earned. I felt guilty about having lied to Bob.

"That's not too bad," he said. "All the same, I still think you're pretty barmy. I had lied to him before. Why don't you forget about Stinker altogether, and come and work for me?" he repeated.

"All right, of course I'll work for you, but on one condition, and one condition only."

"On what condition?"

"That you rise through the echelons of medicine and become a consultant surgeon, with an array of swivelling, leather-studded chairs, and a splendid, leather-studded couch in Harley Street."

"Don't be so stupid!" said Bob angrily, adding, "All right, so you don't want to work for me at the *Mirror*? You know very well that I will not undergo any medical training. I'm a bloody newspaper proprietor!"

"All right, Bob," I said, "I was only joking."

"Come on. Let me show you round the *Mirror*," he said.

When we left Bob's office, I noticed his appearance more clearly, in the lights on the ceiling in the reception area. I had never seen him looking so attractive since he was young.

As he got older and noticed the odd white hair on his head, he asked his barber to dye his hair as black as a raven's wing. The jet black dye looked phoney and also made his appearance seem harsh, not to mention crude.

Before I saw him at the *Mirror*, his barber must have pointed this out to him. Instead of looking as if his hair had been painted with jet black boot polish, it looked dark brown instead.

I don't know whether this was due to the overhead lights or not, but the dark brown colour looked as if the dye had been subtly mixed with a slightly red tint.

He had lost some weight and his shock of thick hair was a bit dishevelled. His hazel eyes were brighter, suggesting that he was happier. The only thing which struck me as being strange, once we had left his office, was the fact that his eyes failed to focus on an object for more than a second at a time. He had noticed my slightly inebriated state and held me by the hand, so that I wouldn't fall over. He did not tick me off for being drunk in his offices. I thought that was really nice of him.

I had no idea that he was dying, through lack of oxygen to his brain, and I did not notice that his breathing was rather laboured. Nor did I realize that, in only about eighteen months' time, his thinking processes would deteriorate to such a terrifying extent, that his behaviour would be adversely affected.

I can give an example of his deteriorating condition. During the last month of his life, someone sharing a lift with him at the *Mirror*, noticed that there was something seriously wrong with him. This unfortunate person waited for him to get out at the ground floor and said, "Have a nice day, Mr Maxwell!"

Bob turned to whoever it was and shouted, "I'll have whatever kind of day I want!" Had he been younger and healthier, he would have been much more friendly.

There was another incident this time on a plane, which was already in the sky. Bob found it too hot and tried to break the window with his shoe. He had to be forcibly restrained.

Bob took me to a large office, occupied by the *Mirror*'s editors. He was still holding my hand, as I had not sobered up. It was a nice, open-plan office. When Bob came into the room, the editors, who had been lolling, suddenly threw themselves into their work. Those who had no work to do, hurriedly busied themselves. I found the power that their boss wielded over them, to be devastatingly attractive.

He addressed the editors collectively and said what he always said, when he introduced me to anyone. He said I had joined the Communist Party, had taught myself Russian and had gone to Russia alone, against my parents' wishes when I was in my teens.

"Come and meet Mr Whittaker, who is our Royal Correspondent," said Bob. I shook Mr Whittaker's hand.

Bob continued to address Mr Whittaker.

"I've just offered Eleanor a job on the *Mirror*? She's turned me down. She turned me down before."

"Oh, indeed, Mr Maxwell?" said the bemused Mr Whittaker.

Bob raised his voice and his words reverberated round the office.

"Do you know why she's turned my offer down? She has turned me down, because she prefers working in hospitals. She likes the blood and guts. She's only at home in mortuaries and operating theatres. She prefers the company of the dead to that of the living." Some of the *Mirror* editors cleared their throats. It was unusual for Bob to speak at such length.

"What story are you running at the moment?" Bob asked one of the female editors.

"I'm running a story about the actress (I can't remember her name) who became a born-again Christian," replied the woman.

"Good," said Bob, "It's never too late to turn to God."

"Do you ever cover stories about medical secretaries being persecuted by temps?" I asked the woman.

Bob put his hand on my shoulder. "We're not going to discuss that boring woman, whom you call 'Stinker' in here," he said sternly.

I shook hands with quite a few editors, before Bob escorted me out of their office, still holding my hand.

"Would you like to see the *Mirror* coming off the presses, Eleanor?" asked Bob. I told him I would.

When the paper was coming off the presses, the machines made an unbroken, rhythmic noise, as they moved the editions from one level to another. The sight was not unlike the birth of thousands of children. I was hypnotized.

"Have you got a car?" asked Bob suddenly.

"No. There's no-where to park in London, blast it!"

"That's all right. I'll get one of my drivers to take you home."

"That's really very kind of you. Are you sure?"

"Stop saying I'm very kind. I'm not kind."

A car pulled up in the yard and I staggered into it.

Just before I did so Bob kissed me "goodbye". This time, he kissed me on the mouth. It was a short kiss, as opposed to the lingering kisses of lovers.

"Goodbye, Pussycat and thank you for my prezzie. Remember, you've *got* to get rid of Stinker! Take action as soon as you see her tomorrow morning."

"I will, Bob, and thank you so much for showing me round the *Mirror*."

That was the last time I saw him.

The driver was friendly throughout the journey. He told me that he had once driven Ghislaine, to represent her father at Marjorie Proops's husband's funeral.

* * *

I arrived at my office at nine o'clock sharp the following day. My mind was busy with plans to get rid of Stinker. Bob had given me strength. She arrived at nine forty-five. She was carrying an umbrella, although it hadn't been raining. "Good morning," she said, and launched into a repulsive display of sniffing, as well as complaints about other passengers on her bus.

I looked ostentatiously at my watch. "Good *afternoon*," I said. "Are you not aware that your hours are nine till five?"

"I don't write 'nine till five' on my time-sheet," she replied.

"I don't give a fuck what you write on your blasted, bloody time-sheet! Why the hell can't you get in at nine o'clock, like everybody else?"

"My bus was late."

"Oh? Has your bus been late every morning since you started to work here? If so, why can't you get on an earlier bus?"

"Stop questioning me, will you?"

"I have the authority to question you. I am a permanent member of staff. You are not. When an employment agency sends you somewhere, that agency always says, 'The hours are nine till five.'"

"If I were to complain to your agency, and say that you never come to work on time, they would probably cross you off their books."

Stinker sat down and started to scratch out a lottery card.

"What are you doing?" I asked aggressively.

"Well, I was just scratching out a lottery card. I won't be a minute."

"Did your agency tell you they would be paying you to find out whether or not you'd won the lottery?"

"You won't have this power over me when I become permanent," said Stinker.

Her voice was so high-pitched then, that it would have been able to shatter glass.

I felt Bob's strength within me once more. I actually wanted to murder Stinker.

I sneered at her. "When do you propose to apply for your job on a permanent basis?" I asked her pompously.

"That is between myself and the doctors."

"Which doctors?" I asked, although I knew the answer to my question.

"Dr Beria" (name changed), Dr Cattell and Professor Raine."

"Why do you wish to share an office with me?" I asked. "I certainly don't enjoy sharing an office with you. Quite apart from that, your typing is absolutely terrible and your spelling is even worse. You have no idea how to write decent English."

Stinker changed the subject.

"Do you know the name of my agency?" she asked me cautiously.

I knew the name of Stinker's agency. It was 'Smile'. I refrained from answering her question. If she thought I was about to complain about her to Smile, she would have realized the urgency of her applying for her job on a permanent basis. I thought of complaining to them about her there and then. Finally, I decided not to do so.

"Do you know the name of my agency?" Stinker repeated.

"I don't know and I don't care!" I shouted.

"Incidentally, one of the secretaries in the ground floor office, gave me your home phone number," said Stinker.

"So what?" I asked.

"You took most of yesterday off, because you were feeling ill. Everyone said you'd gone home, so I assumed you would have been in your flat. When I rang you, between about six o'clock and seven o'clock, there was no reply. Where were you?" asked Stinker.

"Mind your own fucking business!"

"There are several things about you that I can't stand. One

160

is that you open the mail with a flick-knife. The other is that you swear like a trooper," Stinker began.

"Another thing, I went through your drawers while you were allegedly off sick, and I couldn't help noticing some letters, which were from Robert Maxwell. I've read them all and their tone suggests that he is a great friend of yours. You do have strange tastes in friends, don't you? He really is an *awful* man."

"Watch it, Stinker! I know where you live. I've had you tailed. If you continue to provoke me in this way, your husband will shortly be attending your funeral," I said, my voice low and menacing like the voices of the Krays.

There was a silence. "If I were to list *all* the things about you that I can't stand, I'd need to write a fucking book!" I shouted. "Ever since you started to work in this office, I have been so miserable that I have had to consult a psychiatrist once a week." I continued,

"You are cantankerous, common, interfering, intrusive, genteel and thoroughly obnoxious! Not only that, you stoop low enough to read other people's mail.

"If I have to work in the same office as you, for so much as a week longer, I propose to contact the Department of Human Resources and offer them my statement of resignation!"

Professor Anthony Raine, one of the three doctors on our firm, liked and respected me, and resented the fact that a mere temp had been making me suffer so much.

He had been eavesdropping from outside the door. He had heard all my furious words. Although he was too discreet to mention it, he had disliked Stinker, ever since he had tripped over her opened umbrella in the corridor.

"This wouldn't have happened, if you'd looked where you were going," she had said cheekily.

Professor Raine asked the department's administrator to ring Stinker's agency and say that her services were no longer required. Stinker was told that they would be crossing her off their books,

161

because of complaints about her from people in other hospitals. Her agency also told her not to come to work the following day.

I arrived the next day at nine o'clock. I met Professor Raine in the kitchen. He was making tea.

"It's all right, Eleanor. She's not coming back. She's been sacked," he said, adding, "Also, her agency are crossing her off their books."

I was relieved at first when I heard the news. I thanked Professor Raine for having saved me from a fate worse than death.

I went to my office and wrote a letter to Bob (in English, this time). I thanked him profusely for having shown me round the *Mirror*. I also told him the glorious news that I would never be seeing Stinker again. I told him I had got rid of her.

I knew I had pleased him. For the first time for several months, I went to sleep as soon as my head hit the pillow.

I bitterly regretted the fact that Stinker had actually been crossed off her agency's books, however. It had never been my intention to punish her quite so severely. All I wanted to do was to get her out of my hair.

* * *

It was beginning to get dark on the afternoon of Tuesday, 5th November, 1991. I was still working at Barts. It was a long time after Stinker had left. My workmate after her dismissal, was called "Doris Nicholson". She was my best friend ever, but she was a bit aggressive and quarrelled with the management, so she had to move to another department. My present workmate was Irish. Her name was Rita Cassidy. She was a nice girl but she could be rather fiery at times.

Rita was busy with her computer and I was chatting up a man in the kitchen.

"What's your name?" I asked him.

"Tom Conlon." He, too, was Irish. I could tell by his accent.

"Tom O'Condom, did you say?" Tom laughed.

"No, Tom Conlon."

"What do you do, Tom?" I asked him.

"I'm a stretcher-bearer. I carry dead bodies most of the time."

"How amusing!"

Tom told me he had received more than one warning from the Department of Human Resources, because he had been drunk in charge of a dead body. He had one more warning to go. After that, he would be dismissed.

Tom did not take his predicament seriously, which I thought was strange. He told me that he had a large family, all of whom were Catholics, living in Kilburn. He had no other income and few friends. This meant that in the event of his being sacked from Barts, he would have been forced to go onto benefits. That is, if he failed to find another job.

Tom also had cirrhosis of the liver. He and I were drinking tea, and he was boasting to me about the many fights that he had been involved in in pubs.

"No one ever provokes a Conlon!" he said assertively.

I had found a pair of dark glasses in one of the drawers in the kitchen.

"Put these on, Tom," I said. He did so.

"They suit you. You should wear them all the time."

"I think someone's calling you," he said suddenly.

"Who?"

"Someone in your office, I think."

"I'll go and see what they want. I'll be back in a few minutes' time," I said. I had been enjoying my conversation with Tom and was irritated by the interruption.

It was Rita who was calling me. That afternoon, she and I had had what Reggie Kray would have called "a little bit of an argument." She had insisted on singing a well-known, horribly morbid song called *Blowing in the Wind*. I have always associated this song with the onset of bad luck.

"As a penalty for singing that awful song, you're to answer the phones all afternoon," I said.

"There's a call for you," said Rita. "It's your brother, Adrian."

"Hullo." I could tell by the tone of Adrian's voice that he was about to announce sad news.

"I'm afraid I've got some rather startling news for you," he said.

"Yes?"

"It's about Robert Maxwell."

"What's happened?"

"He's gone missing."

"Missing? Missing from where?"

"The news has just come through from *Reuters*. He was on *The Lady Ghislaine*, his boat. They think he may have got up during the night, and gone out onto the deck. He may have accidentally fallen overboard, or I'm afraid it's possible that he might have committed suicide," said Adrian.

"Suicide? That's impossible," I shouted. "Hasn't the boat been searched?" I added.

"Yes, repeatedly."

"What about the lavatories?"

"They've been searched as well," said Adrian.

"This is ridiculous," I said. "Supposing one of the lavatories was locked? No crew member would have dared to bang on the door, to see if his boss were on the other side of it."

"No. It's not like that," said Adrian patiently. "It looks as if he's been drowned. Either that, or he's deliberately taken his life. I made this call, so that you wouldn't see the information on the news-stands on your way home."

I fell unconscious, but I wasn't unconscious for long. When I came round, I heard Rita shouting at Adrian. At that moment, I wasn't sure what was going on. I was disorientated.

"Stop making so much noise," I said.

Rita continued, "You should never have rung your sister up

in the first place. You should have come to the hospital and told her whatever the bad news is face to face. You really are being very irresponsible."

"How dare you speak to my brother like that!" I shouted. I snatched the receiver from Rita's hand.

"Why don't you get a taxi and come to my office?" said Adrian.

"I won't be able to come for another two hours, at least."

"Why so long?"

"I've had a shock. I'm going to the nearest pub with my friend, Doris Nicholson."

"All right, I'll go home. Let me know if you need anything," said Adrian.

"Thank you so much."

"It's all right. This is what brothers are for."

Rita left, at five o'clock sharp, because she had planned to go to a Guy Fawkes party with her boyfriend. I thought this was a funny sort of party for an Irish Catholic to attend.

I rang Doris up and told her the news. She came straight to my office, together with a junior doctor called "Melanie Shaw", who was very sympathetic. Tom, also came to the office after Rita had left. He had heard a lot of shouting and had wondered why I hadn't returned to the kitchen, within a few minutes, as I had promised. Doris told him I had had a shock. He could tell by the expression on my face that I had received sad news. He was still wearing the dark glasses which I had said suited him.

"Why are you wearing those ridiculous dark glasses in November?" asked Doris.

"Eleanor said they suited me," replied Tom.

"You'd better go home now, Tom," said Doris. "It's after five o'clock. Besides, I'm leaving with Eleanor. I think it would be better if you didn't come with us."

It took me some time to realize that Bob had probably been drowned. I was taken to the nearest pub by Doris Nicholson and

Melanie Shaw. I think the pub was called *The Red Lion* but I don't know for sure.

I ordered two double gin and tonics, which eased my grief a little. A very pleasant man standing by the bar, kindly, if somewhat unwisely, bought me more gin. He was the actor, Bob Hoskins.

There was an unpleasant atmosphere of jubilation in the pub. Readers of *The Evening Standard*, some sitting on chairs, others on barstools, rattled their copies of the paper in the air, in an attempt to find the inside pages. The headlines kept flashing in front of me. The most disagreeable thing of all, was the joy with which these people reacted to the tragic news:

MAXWELL IS DEAD

MAXWELL DIES AT SEA

MAXWELL MAY HAVE BEEN DROWNED

Some hooligans, aged between about twenty-five and thirty-five, even went so far as to dance a karaoke across the pub floor. Some of them chanted, "The bastard's dead! The bastard's dead!"

There were no mobile phones in those days. There was only a pay-phone near the bar. Bob Hoskins very kindly gave me some coins.

I rang Headington Hill Hall and asked to be put through to Betty. I wanted to tell her how shocked and horrified I was to hear the news. Jay Miller, Betty's secretary at the time, told me that she and Philip had already flown to Tenerife to identify Bob.

The longer Doris, Melanie, Bob Hoskins, and I stayed in the pub, the more crowded and noisy it became. A drunk, aged about fifty, stumbled over an elderly lady in a wheelchair near the bar. "Whay-hay-hay-hay-hay-hay!" he shouted. He was waving *The Evening Standard* in the air, showing the paper's front page which was splashed with the sad news.

Doris was drinking gin like myself. She had always been terribly loyal to me. She threw the contents of her glass into the drunk's face. He staggered towards her and fell over. (Alas, Doris is now dead. She died of pulmonary fibrosis years later.)

Almost everybody in the room chanted the words, "The monster's dead, the monster's dead!" The scene was like the beginning of a Shakespearian tragedy.

Faithful Doris and I shouted obscene abuse at these people. We certainly taught them a few new words. The landlord came over to us all and asked us to leave. Further, he told us never to come onto the premises again.

The late Dr Victor Chaim Ratner, whom I used to address as "Ratty", very cleverly worked out where I would be drinking that evening. He drove to the pub in his dented old Bentley.

Ratty had been a dear friend of mine since my teens. I was heartbroken when he died in 1993.

I was what is known as "legless" later on on the night of 5th November.

He helped me into his car, and told me that he would be admitting me to hospital, so that I could be treated for shock. That is to say, I was to be given endless cups of sweet tea, together with Diazepam (Valium).

Ratty had me admitted to the Charring Cross Hospital, a National Health hospital. That was the only place where there was a bed.

A great friend of mine, Elisa Segrave, who is an extremely talented writer, and who has always given me flattering reviews, was, co-incidentally, on the same ward that I was on. She was convalescing from an operation for breast cancer. I didn't know at the time that she would be writing a book, describing her illness, and the patients she had met during her incarceration in hospital.

Her book is entitled *Diary of a Breast*, which is witty, page-turning and written, arrestingly, in the present tense. She has changed the names of her characters. I am represented by a raving mad, drunken harridan, called Joan, who makes obscene and abusive phone calls to journalists, and who shouts about her regret that she will not be able to go to Jerusalem, to attend Robert Maxwell's funeral. This woman uses such unbelievably filthy language, that some of her words are unknown, even to me. Elisa's book turned out to be a bestseller.

Unfortunately unlike Elisa, I was no ideal patient on the ward. I never am whenever I'm in hospital. When everybody was being given their night medication, the night nurse offered me a drug, which I was not accustomed to, called *Temazepam*. This belongs to the *Benzodiazepine* family and is addictive.

Ratty had spoken to the nurses about me on my admission. He had ordered homeopathic sleeping pills, which he had had specially flown over from Paris. Unlike *Temazepam*, these pills were not additive.

"I'm only going to take the pills which my Harley Street doctor has had flown over from Paris." I said, my voice raised.

"'Ere! 'Ark at Lady Muck!" shouted a middle-aged woman. Her bed was on the nicest part of the ward, by the window, with a spectacular view of London. I was reminded of the view of London from the top floor of the *Mirror*.

I refused the night nurse's offer of *Temazepam* and continued to demand the pills which Ratty had ordered from Paris.

"It's *Temazepam* or nothing," said the night nurse.

"In that case, would you please bring the pay-phone onto the ward, so that I can ring Dr Ratner personally?" I said.

"It's too late at night for phones to be brought onto the ward," she replied.

"In that case, would you please ring him up from the phone in your office." I gave her Ratty's number which I knew by heart.

The night nurse lost her temper.

"This is not an amusement arcade!" she shouted.

"I don't recall suggesting that it was."

"You may not realize this, but I have got other things to do and other patients to see," said the night nurse.

"My taxes pay for patients to be treated with consideration and compassion. This comes within your job description, which advocates courtesy and flexibility," I began. I added, "If I were to report you to your Department of Human Resources, you could easily get an official written warning. I've taken your name from your lapel."

The night nurse disappeared from the ward and returned twenty minutes' later.

"I've phoned Dr Ratner's rooms, and all I could get was an answer service," she said. "I suggest you take the *Temazepam*, like everybody else on the ward. Also, if you make any more noise, I shall have to refer you to the Duty Psychiatrist."

"I don't need a bloody psychiatrist!" I shouted. "All I want are the homeopathic pills which Dr Ratner has had flown over from Paris."

"'Course, you needs a bloomin' psychiatrist, Lady Muck!" remarked the disagreeable woman in the bed by the window.

I suddenly realized that Nicky had very kindly brought me two bottles of Claret. He had come to visit me on my admission. I had hidden the bottles under the bed.

After the night nurse had left the ward, the lights were dimmed. I got out of bed and opened one of the bottles by pushing the cork down into the bottle. This was not easy to do.

Eventually, Nicky's wine made me sleepy. I was about to doze off, when I heard the night nurse speaking from her office. She had a loud voice and I could hear her words clearly.

"Mrs Cullen, will you please take your sister away from this hospital?"

It was then four o'clock in the morning! The timing of the call must have terrified Harriet. The night nurse continued, "I'm sorry, Mrs Cullen, but your sister is causing a major breach of the peace. She is being extremely difficult and disruptive."

The night nurse came over to see me. I had managed to hide the opened bottle of wine under the bed.

"I can't tolerate any more of this behaviour, Miss Berry," she said, "Your sister will be collecting you in about half an hour's time."

"You rang her up at four o'clock in the bloody morning!"

"I was faced with no choice," said the night nurse.

"Robert Maxwell is dead," I said aggressively.

"Maybe that's just as well." I sneered at her.

She walked over to a mirror and adjusted her dishevelled hair, as if she had been expecting a lover.

Harriet appeared within about half an hour's time. I felt extremely guilty because I had caused her sleep to be disturbed, but she was pretty tolerant in the circumstances. Had I been her, I would have refused to come to the hospital. She didn't seem to be at all concerned about having been woken up. Her conduct was exemplary.

However, she looked under the bed and saw the two bottles of Claret, the second one nearly empty. She was terrified that I was going to be sick.

"Is my sister going to be sick?" she asked urgently and pinned the night nurse against a wall. It was the best thing she had ever done in her life, thought I.

Harriet is a sturdy old soul. Her nerves are good, although like me, she is prone to outbursts of temper. She never panics in a crisis, in the way I do, but there is one thing that repulses her beyond oblivion and that is the sight of someone being sick. She has a pathological phobia about this.

"I don't know, Mrs Cullen," replied the night nurse. "She's had a great deal to drink, even before she was admitted to this hospital. Apparently, your brother, Nicholas, brought some wine in and your sister has drunk quite a lot of it."

"Oh, dear!" Harriet guided me along the corridor.

"Be honest with me," she said, "Is there any chance at all of your being sick?"

"No."

"It was really naughty of Nicky to bring you all that wine. I'm going to be absolutely livid with him, if you're sick, and I'm going to take you straight to his house."

"I'm not going to be sick!"

Harriet and her delightful husband, an Argentinian writer, called "Martin" (pronounced Martine), looked after me for a few days and took me to the cinema every evening.

Sometimes, I played with my nephews, Miguel and Mingo, then aged about eight and nine. Harriet was adamant that I should not leave the house alone.

"Why not?" I asked.

"Because, in your present psychological state, I wouldn't put it past you to take a taxi to the offices of *The Sun*, and slit someone's throat with one of your fucking flick-knives. It's the sort of thing you might do, when you're in a bait."

I laughed out loud. This was the first time I had laughed, since Tom Conlon had boasted about his violent outbursts in pubs.

* * *

Harriet and Martin lived in Chelsea. Opposite the kitchen, across a stretch of grass, is a house inhabited by a group of men, all of whom are as gay as crickets. Their bathroom has a wide, uncurtained window. Sometimes, these men touch each other while standing by the window. Apparently, they like their sexual activities to be witnessed by members of the public.

Harriet keeps bottles of spirits in her kitchen. I unscrewed a bottle of *Gordon's* gin, and poured it into a glass, together with some tonic water. I took a swig and stared at Harriet's exhibitionist neighbours, two of whom were standing naked by their bathroom window and indulging in bizarre frolics.

Harriet came into the kitchen.

"What the hell do you mean by drinking at ten o'clock in the morning? Anyone would think you actually *wanted* to get cirrhosis of the liver, like so many Smiths and Berrys!"

"I was just looking at your eccentric neighbours," I replied. As I spoke, I looked at one of them and waved.

Harriet was acutely embarrassed.

"Don't do that. I have to *live* here!"

After breakfast, Harriet, Martin and I read the papers. It was comforting to read about Bob, before the gutter press turned on him.

The following day, I was due to see Dr Peter Rohde, a Harley Street psychiatrist. He really is a fucking old woman. By the time I arrived in Harley Street, I was inebriated. Instead of going straight to his rooms, I went into the wrong building. I entered a room on the ground floor, which was identical to Rohde's consulting room from the outside.

The man I faced was bending over a supine patient. When he saw me, he stood up straight. He was too startled to ask me who I was and what I was doing in his consulting room.

He was, in fact, a dentist but I was too befuddled to realize this. He was about five foot eight inches tall, wore outmoded, black-rimmed glasses and was as bald as a billiard ball.

"Are you Dr Peter Rohde, the psychiatrist?" (I had once seen Rohde before but I couldn't remember what he looked like.)

"Do I look like a psychiatrist?" asked the dentist.

"Yes, as a matter of fact, you do."

There was a silence, while the dentist gathered his wits together. His patient turned round, her eyes almost bulging out of their sockets.

"Who are you?" the dentist eventually managed to mutter.

I began to talk incoherently and at length about Bob and, for some reason, about his relationship with his father.

The dentist continued to look startled.

"Will you go away, please," he said mildly.

Rohde was waiting for me in the street. He was on the pavement, leaning against the railings. The dentist must have spoken to him already. Rohde looked at me, as if he had left his entire family in a burning building.

"Have you harmed anyone, Miss Berry?" he asked. His voice was almost as high-pitched as Stinker's.

"No," I said.

Rohde was tallish, clean-eyed and pugnacious-looking. He looked rather like the serial-killer, Dennis Nilson.[14*] Although Rohde saw private patients, he was a militant left-winger, and his wife, Jennifer, used to deliver parcels of food to the women demonstrating at Greenham Common. The most noteworthy thing about Rohde was his car. It was a turquoise 2CV. He used to leave this heinous heap of flashing, sky-blue metal in the streets, together with copious notes on the windscreen, to traffic wardens in a flowing italic hand.

Rohde's consulting room was extremely dingy. He had borrowed it from a consultant urologist. Books about urology lay on his desk and photographs of a hunt adorned the mantelpiece.

"Why have you got books about urology in your consulting room, when you're a psychiatrist?" I asked.

"Er... Mind your own business," he replied. He added, "What actually happened between you and that dentist?"

"Not a lot. Mistook him for you, didn't I?"

"Is that supposed to be a backhanded compliment?"

"Neither a compliment nor an insult."

"Did you know he'd been ill?" asked Rohde.

"How the hell could I have known whether the blasted bloody dentist had been ill or not?" I asked, my voice raised.

"No. Did you know that the gentleman had been ill?"

"What gentleman?"

"Mr Maxwell."

At that time, I was unaware of the fact that Bob had been ill.

Interestingly, Ghislaine, when being interviewed by a glossy magazine, had denied that her father had been ill. She was adamant that he had been murdered.

14* The late Dennis Nilson was gay, murdered homeless men and did so, "for company". Finally, he cut up their bodies and put them down drains which eventually got blocked.

Surely, she must have realized if he was ill. Even if she had not seen him, up to the time of his death surely someone, like her mother, would have kept her informed. Perhaps, she had forced herself into denial and had refused to accept that he was dying.

"He was never ill. He was murdered," I said bitterly. "Someone must have come up behind him and pushed him into the water."

I don't remember the rest of the consultation. I was too intoxicated. I fell over and couldn't get up. I'd like to inform the reader that I only become inebriated if I have had a bereavement.

Shortly after the consultation, I received a huge bill from Rohde, accompanied by a rather hysterical letter. It was dated sometime in November, 1991:

"Dear Miss Berry,

Please do not drink before you come into my consulting room in future. I've got a very bad back. If there had not been someone on the premises to lift you up, I would have sustained even more damage to my back, than I have already.

"You may not be aware of this, but you made amorous advances towards me, while you were under the influence of intoxicating liquor. You effectively pulled me down to the floor on top of you, and caused me yet another muculo-skeletal dislocation, which has made it necessary for me to wear a John Bell and Croyden's corset.

Yours sincerely,
Peter Rohde
Consultant Psychiatrist

I wrote a humorous reply to his effete letter:

"Dear Dr Rohde,

*Do you think Rhett Butler sustained a musculo-skeletal dislocation
when he was carrying Scarlett O'Hara from the flames of Atlanta?
Do you think he had to wear a John Bell and Croyden's corset as a
result?*

*Had this been necessary, the manuscript of Gone with the Wind
would have been rejected by every publisher in the States."*

*Yours sincerely,
Eleanor Berry
BA Hons: English*

Rohde lacked a sense of humour. I decided I would not give
him up completely but that I would two-time him with another
psychiatrist. Rhode is a lounge-lizard Lenin and I can't stand
lounge-lizard Lenins.

On a previous occasion, before Bob's death, I had consulted
Rohde and had expressed my fantasies about Bob. "He is involved
in your infatuation for him," said Rohde. "Technically I ought to
inform him personally and will do so."

I flew into a rage. "If you dare to approach this man to talk
to him about me, by Christ, I'll have you duffed," I shouted. I
walked slowly towards Rohde who was terrified I was going to
rape him. He shielded his fucking gear with a rolled-up copy of
the Guardian.

"You take *The Guardian* but you see private patients in Harley
Street," I said, adding, "Do you know what punishments awaited
hypocrites in Dante's *The Divine Comedy?*" I can't remember
Rohde's reply but he certainly didn't say anything particularly
original.

Ratty referred me to another Harley Street psychiatrist. I
will not give his name. Nor will I give the street number of the

building in which his consulting rooms can be found. I will refer to him as "Dr Jones", which is not his real name. He is not related to Nella Jones, the charlatan clairvoyant whom I will speak about later.

Dr Jones is to die for, he is so good-looking! I am loathe, to describe his appearance. Although he does not resemble Bob in any way, he is profoundly attractive all the same. I still see him to this day and he always allows me to lick his hands. I hope he will permit me to go further than this one day.

* * *

I was staying in my flat at the time of the following incident. I had left Harriet's house. I was driving up Park Lane towards Marble Arch. It was about three-thirty in the afternoon. Inadvertently, I drove through a red light, just opposite the Dorchester Hotel. I wasn't concentrating.

I was excited because I was about to see Dr Jones.

A panda car flashed at me from behind and I pulled into the side. A policeman got out of the panda car and walked over to where I had parked. I wound down the window. He was alone.

"Why do you think I stopped you?" he asked.

"I'm afraid I don't know."

"You went through a red light."

"Oh, I had an idea it was amber," I replied, adding, "That Desk Sergeant of yours, is he a pretty tough egg?" I could afford to be light-hearted, as I hadn't had anything to drink that day. I continued, "Mind you, if no-one ever broke the law, the police wouldn't be able to earn their living, would they?"

"This is not a time for joking. Also, you're wrong. You went through a red light. It wasn't amber," said the policeman.

"Oh, dear. Would you be prepared to accept an apology?"

My question startled him. There was a silence before he spoke again.

"Have you got your driving licence with you?" he asked.

"Yes. I've just had a bereavement. I was a close friend of the late Robert Maxwell's." I didn't realize until later that I had given the man unsolicited information.

"Oh, yes, the crook."

"Indeed, he was *not* a crook. He most certainly was not! According to his widow, he wept during the sex act," I said nonsensically.

"Have you got your driving license with you?" repeated the policeman impatiently.

I handed it to him.

"Is your name Eleanor Berry?"

"Yes."

"What is your occupation?"

"I'm a medical secretary. Most of the time, I write books, though."

"Why are you not at work?"

"I've been given compassionate leave."

"Are you Miss or Mrs Berry?"

"Miss."

"I'll let you off, this time, Miss Berry. I advise you to be a bit more observant in future. Where are you going?"

"Up Harley," I said.

"Do you mean Harley Street?"

"Yes."

"Have you got a medical issue, then?"

"No. I'm just going to lick my psychiatrist's hands."

The policeman cleared his throat.

"Do you know something, Miss Berry?" he began.

"What?"

"You're a little bit eccentric."

"I beg your pardon, Officer?"

"On your way, before I change my mind and decide to nick you."

I arrived at Dr Jones's consulting rooms just before four o'clock. He allowed me to lick his hands once more. They tasted sweet, as if he had smeared honey onto them.

"May I ask you a personal question?" he asked.

"What's your question?"

"Did you have sexual relations with the late Robert Maxwell?"

"I'll only answer your question, if you allow me to suck your cock," I replied.

I also consulted an American therapist. His name is Dr Mortimer Schatzman and he lives in North London. He is very dry. On one occasion, I said, "I drove to the Maxwells' house which is no longer inhabited. It had been raining heavily. I went onto the lawn. I knelt down on the wet earth and I recited *The Raven*."

"So what?" replied Dr Schatzman impatiently.

His words caused me to laugh hysterically. I continued to laugh on and off for about two days. Although he is comical, I did not consult him again, because of his enormous bills

* * *

Private Eye produced a singularly offensive front cover, the week after Bob had died. There was a close-up of the photograph of his burial on the Mount of Olives. One pall-bearer had a caption coming out of his mouth, saying, "Here lies Robert Maxwell." The next pall-bearer had a caption which said, "He lied everywhere." Another caption said, "All twenty stone of him." A caption from the body said, "You're all fired." The other captions were even more tasteless.

I suggested to Ratty, (the late Dr Ratner), that we both turn up at the offices of *Private Eye*, unannounced, and descend on Ian Hislop, the magazine's editor. Bob always referred to him as "Mr Pigslop" and to his former partner, Richard Ingrams, as "Mr Wigwam."

Ratty was not particularly tall. He had blond hair and large blue eyes. He felt as strongly as I did about the magazine's heinous cover. He, too, had been a friend of Bob's, so he agreed to accompany me to the magazine's offices. I had once introduced Ratty to Bob when he (Ratty) had complained bitterly because his young wife, Gida[15*] had been harassed by cameramen from *The News of the World* when she was pregnant. Ratty took a taxi to the offices of the *Mirror*.

"Have you come to see me via Eleanor Berry?" Bob asked him.

"Yes. She's a good friend of mine."

"She's a good friend of mine, as well."

According to Ratty, the rest of their conversation had taken place in Hebrew. I can't remember the outcome of the conversation, although Ratty had told me about it at the time.

* * *

The front office of *Private Eye* was filthy. It looked like the inside of a Third World shack. A receptionist-come-secretary, was manning a 1960s switchboard. I was dressed, from head to foot in black leather. Ratty was wearing a pin-striped suit.

The walls of the office were peppered from top to bottom with photographs of staff parties and of Ian Hislop, who occupied the limelight. In the fridge, which I was invited to open, was a bottle of apple juice with a floating fungus on top of it.

The secretary was pleasant and sympathetic towards Ratty and me although she didn't strike me as being very intelligent. I told her we wanted to speak to Hislop urgently. I introduced us, giving false names.

15* The author came to blows with Gida and appeared in court after Ratty's death. The author is not giving further details.

"Take a seat, please," she said. She directed us to a black, leather sofa, which had seen better days. It had a large hole in the middle of it, from which springs could easily have cut through someone's clothing.

In one corner of the office, was a pile of previous issues of *Private Eye*, with coffee stains and cigarette burns on them. Cigarette butts in brimming, plastic ashtrays and a half-empty cup of tea, lay on a chipped occasional table.

"What would you like to discuss with Mr Hislop?" asked the secretary. I had an answer ready:

"I was a cleaner on *The Lady Ghislaine* on Maxwell's last journey. I know how he died. He didn't fall off the boat accidentally. Nor did he deliberately take his life. Nor was he pushed. There was another woman with me," I added vaguely.

The secretary took a gulp of tea. I assumed she had let it get cold, judging by the expression on her face, once she had swallowed it. There's nothing that nauseates me more than the taste of cold tea, or indeed the sight of someone drinking it.

"Perhaps it would be more appropriate to pull the Maxwell team, rather than to disturb Mr Hislop, who's got to go to a funeral this afternoon," she said.

Doctors in casualty departments of hospitals, use a similar phrase. If a patient's heart stops beating, they say, "Pull the crash team."

"What does, 'Pull the Maxwell team' mean?" I asked.

"It means, 'send for the Maxwellologists'."

"Maxwellologists? Are they people who have graduated in Maxwellology?"

The secretary laughed. "They are the only people who will be able to help you," she said.

"No. We wish to see Mr Hislop personally. We are anxious to speak to him ourselves," I insisted.

Ratty had been sitting on the damaged sofa, reading a long document which described the history of *Private Eye*.

"A fine binding, this?" he forced himself to remark.

It had become apparent that neither Ratty nor I intended to leave the building, until we had spoken to Hislop.

"I'll ring him," said the secretary reluctantly. Hislop answered the phone.

"You can both go up now. Be sure to keep it brief. Otherwise, he'll miss his funeral."

I struggled to keep a straight face. I was feeling quite calm, because I had taken some *Diazepam* or Valium, half an hour before we went upstairs. The stairs were in a shocking state of repair. The carpet covering them was dirty and frayed and the bannisters came away in our hands.

We entered Hislop's office, which, like the front office, was extremely dirty. I went into the room before Ratty did.

"Your office really is awfully dirty! Don't you get a cleaner in in the mornings?" I began.

"What do you want?" asked Hislop in a hostile tone of voice. He looked nervous.

There were two tattered armchairs in the room. Ratty sat down in one of them. I leant over Hislop's desk and showed him a copy of *Private Eye* and its offending cover.

"Have you ever lost someone you loved?" I asked.

"Yes," said Hislop.

"Would you like a picture of this nature, regarding that person, to be published on the cover of a publicly circulated magazine?"

Hislop was startled. "You must know how I felt about Robert Maxwell," he said eventually,

"Had you ever met Robert Maxwell?" I asked aggressively.

"… No."

"In that case, who the hell are you to judge him?"

Ratty surreptitiously removed a menacing-looking cosh from his doctor's bag. He held it with both hands and fondled it with his fingers. I continued to lean over Hislop's desk.

"Do you intend to apologize to Mrs Maxwell, on account of this disgusting outrage?" I asked.

"No," said Hislop quietly.

"Mr Hislop," I said, my voice scarcely above a whisper, "How would you like a carload of the boys?"

Hislop was terrified. He had seen the cosh which Ratty was holding and whitened. He turned to Ratty, which in the circumstances, was quite brave of him.

"You! You!" he shouted at the top of his voice. "What are you doing in my office?"

"I am accompanying the young lady. As I see it, she isn't breaking the law." He continued to fiddle with the cosh.

"What is that strange-looking black thing you're holding?" stuttered Hislop. I had an uncontrollable fit of giggles. I waited for them to subside.

"Nothing you need worry your pretty little head about," I said.

Hislop turned to Ratty once more.

"Will you kindly take this woman out of my office," he said mildly.

"Button your lip, laddie, or we'll sort you Kray-wise!" I said, adding, "You'll be seeing us again, next time at your home. We've had you tailed."

It was such a shame Bob wasn't there to witness the scene. In fact, I felt he had heard everything from beyond the grave.

Ratty and I had completed our business, so we left Hislop's office and walked out of the building into the street. Ratty put the cosh back into his bag.

"What do you think that man did, once we'd left his office?" I asked.

"I should imagine he threw up."

"Do you think he'll call the police?"

"Nah! He won't have time. He's got to go to a funeral, hasn't he?" replied Ratty.

Our visit to Hislop's offices attracted some sections of the press. My father found out and we arranged to have dinner. I knew he was not very pleased.

"What exactly happened in the offices of *Private Eye*?" he asked.

"Not an awful lot," I replied. "Ratty and I arranged to see Hislop."

"Do you mean Dr Ratner?"

"That's right. We went up to his office. We sorted him. Then we left the building."

"What do you mean you sorted him?" he asked urgently. My father had always been conservative and was exceptionally averse to violence.

"Well, we just showed him the magazine, ticked him off and told him to apologize to Mrs Maxwell."

"Did you say anything about a 'carload of the boys'?

"Yes, indeed I did. The reporter got his words mixed up a bit, though I said that one of the Maxwell boys was going to write a letter of complaint to Hislop."

"I see," said my father. He appeared to have become bored with the situation.

* * *

Soon after the *Private Eye* fiasco, there was yet another incident, in which I became involved, to defend Bob's honour, and that of Betty and her children.

A miserable little woman, called "Nella Jones" (no relation to Dr Jones, of course) had set herself up as a "spiritualist". She wrote an article in *The Sun*, about an alleged conversation which she said she had had with Bob from beyond the grave.

Throughout the article, she stressed that he had appeared "chilling" and "evil".She made the mistake of allowing *The Sun* to print her photograph above the article, and had foolishly permitted the paper to print the name of the town she lived in. This enabled me to find out her phone number.

I rang her up at one o'clock in the morning, intending to disturb her sleep.

"Are you Nella Jones?" I asked.

A sleepy voice answered, "Yes" which reassured me that I had woken her up and hence had caught her off guard.

"How much is *The Sun* paying you for the repellent, cowardly article which you've just written about Mr Maxwell?" I demanded.

"That's none of your bloody business! Leave me alone!" Nella shouted.

I pressed on. "Do you know what they did to witches in the seventeenth century?"

"No." Why didn't she hang up? Was she intrigued, by any chance?

"I'll tell you what they did to witches in the seventeenth century. They burnt them alive," I said.

"In the first place, we are not living in the seventeenth century. In the second place, I am not a witch. I am a spiritualist."

"Do the two not come from the same family?" I asked. "You know perfectly well, the dead do not have the power to speak to total strangers. Nor do strangers have the power to speak to the dead!

"Also, you said that, according to Mr Mawell's spirit, the missing pension funds had been transferred to what you referred to as the 'money warehouse'. Were you pissed, or are you naturally a brick short of a load?" I continued, "How dare you refer to Mr Maxwell as a 'crook', when a British court had never found him guilty! I bet you screwed a bomb out of *The Sun*."

"Maxwell *was* a crook!" said Nella.

"And you're not, I suppose."

"Who are you? Kindly give me your name," she said. I thought it was a bit late in the conversation for me to ask for my name.

"I am a distinguished woman of letters. I only spill my identity to those I respect. That doesn't include charlatans, who get loads of money under false pretences, by playing on the superstitions of readers of the gutter press. You then dare to refer to a dead man as a 'crook' when he is unable to defend himself. You are a coward."

We were both taking off. I was reminded of the interminable fencing scene in one of my favourite films, *Theatre of Blood*', starring Vincent Price and Diana Rigg.

"Are you a man or a woman?" Nella asked suddenly. "I can't tell what you are with a voice like that."

"Go fuck yourself, you silly old prostitute!"

Still, the woman failed to hang up.

Nella described Bob's faults and I returned her words with another stream of invective. I referred to her shocking article once more, and stated that I knew where she lived. Finally, I threatened to have her duffed.

I love a good blockbuster, whether it be with a seemingly intelligent man of letters, like Ian Hislop, a common, ignorant temp, like Stinker, or an uneducated writer for *The Sun* like Nella Jones.

* * *

I thought that the adverse publicity about Bob would diminish, as time passed, but it did not. It got much worse. I occupied myself by seeing my friends and relatives, going to the cinema and attacking journalists who had spoken ill of Bob.

Regarding a different matter this time, Ratty, who was scrupulously honest and truthful, told me that he had been dozing off one night, when Bob had spoken to him from beyond the grave.

"Look after Eleanor," he had allegedly said. Ratty woke up with a start. The voice persisted. "This is Bob. Look after Eleanor."

Ratty would never have lied to me about something like that. I believed him and felt much better than I had been feeling earlier. I believe that there are times when the dead actually *can* speak to their living friends, and relatives.

St Bartholomew's Hospital had given me two weeks off on compassionate grounds. It was then that I started to write about my memories of Bob. I wrote three books in all, as I have stated in the "Introduction". This book is the third and final book.

* * *

I will not give the name of the doctor, who employed me at Barts, other than to say that he was devious, selfish and profoundly jealous of my relationship with Bob. He was perilously unattractive to look at. He was more senior than the other two doctors on the firm I worked for, as I said earlier.

I have already referred to him as Dr "Beria" and will continue to refer to him by that name. He wormed his way up the medical ladder, until he somehow managed to become a consultant.

Before Bob's death, he had made it more than apparent that he had been in love with me. More dramatically, he had been absolutely besotted by me. He told everybody that I was the "best" secretary he had ever had.

I had worked for him for five years. He had been particularly nice to me all the time, and had continuously complemented me on my appearance and my so-called "efficiency". I had started to work for him as a temp and later became permanent.

He appealed to my vanity and, I must admit, I did rather like him at first. I worked overtime every evening in order to complete the huge workload. When he noticed I was working overtime, he had always remarked, "Oh, bless you, love!" He addressed women he fancied as "love", which indicates how inordinately common he was.

Dr Beria was born and bred in a provincial town and was an only child. It is possible that his mother, to whom he was extremely close, had spoilt him. He fancied himself as a ladies' man which, because of his hideous physical appearance, was inappropriate. He was approximately five foot six inches tall and walked about, wearing soft-soled shoes, so that he could creep up behind his staff, to make sure they were working.

From the front, he looked like a weather-beaten old bulldog. A pair of unfashionable glasses was jammed onto his face, making him look even more unprepossessing than he would have looked without them.

In profile, he looked fractionally less ugly, however. Although his nose looked as if it had been damaged in a number of fights, it did have some character and was vaguely aquiline in shape.

Mrs Beria, his mother, was a professional singer who, it is likely, spent much of his childhood working.. He was probably raised by a series of *au pair* girls, and, as he had no apparent father figure to discipline him, his spoilt streak and his perpetual desire to be pampered, must have manifested themselves before he could walk.

Dr Beria no doubt became petulant, when his mother had to leave him to go to work. It is often the case that, when only children, particularly boys, become adults, they invariably assume that they are meant to be cosseted by members of the opposite sex, and to be the centre of attention at all times.

Such a specimen was Dr Beria. I had not been intuitive enough to recognize his two-faced personality, his tendency to manipulate his staff behind their backs, his cowardice, his caddishness and his frequent foul manners.

He was rude to timid, young nurses who feared him and, in particular, to his Irish employees. He used to make fun of the fiery Rita Cassidy, by calling her "Noraid", until she terrified him with her awesome temper.

He was also outrageously lecherous. When he thought no-one was looking at him, he was not above putting his hands down the fronts of women's dresses.

He never did this to me, probably because, as well as being in love with me, he was very much in awe of me and respected me. He was pleased with my work at all times. He left scrawled notes on my keyboard saying, "Bless you love! Super work. Very well done."

My first meeting with him was unusual. My agency had sent me to another hospital one Monday morning, but I had been turned away, as I had been double-booked. This often happens to temporary medical secretaries. I then had instructions to go to St Bartholomew's Hospital, where Dr Beria was waiting for a medical secretary. My agency told me to report to him personally. I did as I was told and was in a very bad temper by this time.

"I've had a terrible morning. I've been messed about," I said. "I've been told to report to a Dr Beria."

I no longer cared whether I would be turned away a second time, or not. My spirits were low, although my novel, *Never Alone with Rex Malone*, had just been published, not by Wiedenfeld, but by Harraps Columbus. It had also got quite good reviews.

I saw a pathetic-looking, red-faced, very unattractive man, who was slumped in a swivel chair, staring vacantly into space. I assumed he was a psychiatric patient.

"Where the hell's Dr Beria?" I asked, my voice raised in anger.

The man in the swivel chair struggled to sit up straight. He looked somewhere in his late fifties, early sixties. I thought at first that he was either drunk or drugged.

"I am Dr Beria," he said, in a breathy, classless tone. "Aren't you making rather a lot of noise?"

"I smiled, shook his hand and introduced myself. He had a repulsively limp handshake. I gave him the name of my agency and accompanied him, in a slow-moving lift, to my office on the top floor of the West Wing. It was a homely attic room with natural light blazing in through a big window. I could see part of the Old Bailey, outside the office.

* * *

Two weeks passed. I had completed two long tapes for Dr Beria and, because I wanted to stay in the nice, sunny office, I made sure that my typing was accurate and proof-read my letters twice. There were about thirty-five letters in all.

I left the letters in a leather folder on Dr Beria's desk. His office was next door to mine. I also left some biros, pencils, a pencil-sharpener and some rubbers, which I noticed he had a poor supply of. I put these near the leather folder.

I took the empty tea cup from his desk, tidied his scattered papers and endless copies of *The Lancet*, and left his office, locking the door behind me. I put the key on a hook in the cupboard in the corridor and got on with the tapes, which had been dictated by the other doctors on Dr Beria's firm.

The following day, Dr Beria read my letters and signed them. He rang me on the internal phone and asked me to go to his office. I assumed he was going to tell me that my typing was inaccurate. so I knocked on his door. I was carrying a notebook and a pen, as I thought he might wish to give me dictation.

"Come in," he said.

"You wanted to see me, Dr Beria," I said.

He pointed to the leather folder containing my letters.

"Yes. Please sit down. Is this all your own work?"

"Yes, Dr Beria. Is it all right?"

"It's absolutely superb. Well done, love!"

"Thank you, Dr Beria." He smiled and I returned his smile. I confess, I had developed mild affection for him, combined with pity, due to his ugliness. I was wearing white trousers and a blue and white striped T-shirt.

"Oh, love! Don't you look swish! You've got your sailor suit on, I see. Superb! Superb!"

"Thank you. You will have to excuse me now, Dr Beria. I must get on with the rest of my work," I said.

I felt flattered but a trifle confused. Dr Beria followed me to my office. I noticed that his white coat was too tight.

"I hope you will be staying with us for a long time, love," he said. I noticed his pronunciation of the word "us" as "uzz". This was the only occasion on which he had betrayed his provincial origins.

"I sincerely hope so, Dr Beria. After all, the devil you know is better than the devil you don't."

"Oh, love, you are *not* a devil!" he breathed. He sounded like someone trying to imitate Marilyn Monroe. He added, looking at me with an almost demented expression on his face, "You really *are* an attractive woman."

"Indeed?"

"Oh, love!"

I smiled graciously.

The phone rang.

My phone is ringing and someone might be trying to contact you."

At nine o'clock every morning, I shared a lift with the creepy doctor. The lift was slow but I found it too tiring to walk up four flights of stairs.

The conversation between Dr Beria and myself was roughly the same every morning.

"Oh, love, don't you look swish!"

"You are *too* kind!"

Although Bob's origins were far humbler than Dr Beria's, and his suffering during his childhood was infinitely more severe, Bob always used the word "smashing", rather than "swish", simply because he was less common than Dr Beria.

Dr Beria liked to pose as an educated aristocrat and caused doctors beneath him in rank, to snigger into their hands, and other consultants to ridicule him behind his back.

Apart from me, nurses and other secretaries hated him, because of his rudeness. I, on the other hand, continued to like him, because of his appreciation of my work, and the remarks he invariably made about my appearance. In other words, he flattered my vanity.

* * *

I had been working for Dr Beria for a month. He and I were in the lift one morning. There were two nurses there as well. They were talking about knitting patterns in pronounced south London accents. Neither of them was pretty and their faces were unpainted.

"Good morning, Dr Beria," they said in unison.

Dr Beria ignored them and turned to me.

"What's your surname, Eleanor?" he asked. I was surprised he didn't know what it was already.

"Berry," I replied.

His voice became even oilier than it had been a few seconds before.

"Oh? I take it your father used to own *The Daily Telegraph* and *The Sunday Telegraph*." he said. Although his tone of voice was affable, I did not like the conversation and shifted from one foot to another.

"Yes, that's right," I said abruptly. "How do you know all this about my father?"

"I got my information from *The Sunday Times*. I'm not prying or anything" he added apologetically.

"I don't take *The Sunday Times*," I said coldly, "Or indeed any other papers published by Rupert Murdoch."

Dr Beria suddenly looked as if he had had his face slapped. I regretted having snubbed him. I smiled. There was a pause.

"It's colder than usual for the time of year," I remarked eventually. "Once we get upstairs, I'll make you a pot of tea, Dr Beria," After all, I wanted to keep my job and I was stuck between books at the time. The two nurses fixed me with hostile stares which I returned.

I shared an office with a raunchy girl called "Debbie". She always wore a low-cut, white blouse, showing her cleavage, and a tight, split skirt, made of black linen. Her hair was thick, dark

191

and curly, like a gypsy's. Her voice was girlish and her accent was down-town Croydon.

She and I had in common a love for nineteenth century Russian literature and Russian folk songs, which we talked about when the workload wasn't too heavy.

Dr Beria treated this woman with disdain, and showed resentment of her Croydon accent, but he was never rude to her in front of me.

When I returned to the office after lunch one day, I found that Debbie was subdued and red-eyed.

I asked her what the trouble was.

"Dr Beria came in and shouted at me when you were out."

"What did he say?"

"Give me three sharpened pencils and a rubber. That means immediately, if you wish to stay here."

"How very strange!" I replied.

Not long afterwards, Dr Beria was rude to her again.

Debbie picked up her bag and stormed out of the office, into the corridor.

"I'm leaving. Who the hell do you think you are?"

She left the building, crossed the courtyard and rushed into the street. Dr Beria ran after her, screaming like a madman. His ill-fitting white coat flapped behind him in the wind. He chased her as far as the entrance to St Paul's underground.

"I'm so sorry, Debbie! Oh, love! Don't be upset. I get these funny turns, sometimes. *Please* come back."

Debbie was short of money and could not afford to lose her job. She returned to work.

She had an extremely high sex drive. She fornicated regularly with a junior doctor on Dr Beria's firm, called Dr Chris Jenkins. Jenkins was by no means unique in hating Dr Beria, who frequently patronized him in front of patients during ward rounds.

In the mornings, the two lovers used Dr Beria's private lavatory, to consummate their lust. Because he had been so badly brought-up, Dr Beria had sometimes forgotten to pull the chain. The lovers were undeterred, however, and reached screaming climaxes which could be heard by everyone in the corridor outside the lift.

Sometimes, they used a public phone box outside the mortuary, and were said, by passers-by, to be making enough noise to wake the dead.

It was when they chose to use Dr Beria's office one afternoon, thinking that he would be seeing private patients in Harley Street, that things got a bit dicey.

Two of Dr Beria's private patients had cancelled their appointments, so he returned to his office at Barts prematurely, and found the two lovers having violent sex on his desk.

"There is a time and a place for everything. I feel this is letting down the firm," he said mildly.

Debbie was sacked. Dr Beria did not have the guts to sack her himself. He asked the administrator, Virginia Blake, to do so on his behalf.

* * *

It didn't take long for five years to pass. Debbie was replaced by Nadia, who cracked a lot of dirty jokes. She was replaced by the loathsome Stinker. After Stinker, came Doris, my best friend, and after Doris, came Rita.

There were three secretaries, on the ground floor, who also worked for Dr Beria. We all worked hard and typed the tapes handed to us. We took it in turns to help in the out patients' clinic on Monday afternoons.

Some of the secretaries became bitter, and they resented the fact that Dr Beria favoured me above everyone else. He even allowed me to take Friday afternoons off, on the grounds that I had a "bad" back and needed physiotherapy. I said my "physiotherapist" could only fit me in on Friday afternoons. This meant I could go to the cinema. I have always loved the cinema but I hate going on Saturdays and Sundays.

I knew how much I was hated by the other secretaries, but I didn't care, as long as the boss liked me and continued to allow me to go to the cinema on Friday afternoons.

One morning, I brought a pot of tea into Dr Beria's office. He looked odd but not much odder than usual. He was talking into two telephone receivers at once. I could tell that his wife was at the receiving end of the phone in his right hand, and that his mistress was on the other line.

"I won't be back until one o'clock in the morning. Put my dinner in the microwave and open a bottle of Claret. No, I can't get back earlier, I'm too busy!"

It was obvious that he had just been speaking to his wife. He hung up, without saying "goodbye" and began to speak to his mistress.

"Oh, love! My dearest, dearest love! You asked me who I was speaking to just now. It was only the wife. It's been *too* long. If I don't see you tonight, I'll die!"

Dr Beria finished his phone calls and followed me into my office, which was empty at the time. It was twelve-thirty. My colleague, Rita, had gone to lunch. Dr Beria's cheeks were tear-stained. He looked even more pathetic than usual.

"Oh, love! You've got such beautiful big, brown eyes!" he exclaimed.

"They have always served me well, Dr Beria," I replied.

* * *

Dr Beria's demented love for me lasted until Bob's death in November, 1991. Word had travelled round the department that I had been extremely upset by his demise, and Dr Beria had found out.

We had a new administrator. Her name was Julia Hartley-Cooper. It was she, and not Dr Beria, who suggested that I take compassionate leave.

At first, I liked Julia, until she told me that I had no business taking Friday afternoons off. This meant I couldn't have my weekly outings to the cinema. She found out that I wasn't having physiotherapy after all. An off-duty nurse had seen me in Leicester Square one Friday afternoon.

Dr Beria behaved like a woman spurned after Bob's death. Gone was his blinkered adulation for me. He discovered that another man, and not he, was the object of my adoration.

I had no idea that my happiness at St Bartholomew's Hospital, was to be destroyed, and that my life was to be ruined by a petty, vicious, little man, such as Dr Beria.

I am sure he was aware of his phenomenal ugliness . He had only to look at his reflection in a mirror. When he found out that I had been a close friend of Bob's, the bottom fell out of his sad and tawdry world.

He was a consultant physician, whose duty it was to heal the sick, not to cause an innocent party to become psychologically ill. It was Ratty who had informed me about his sudden hostile attitude towards me. Dr Beria had phoned Ratty. (I had told Dr Beria that Ratty was my G.P.)

"Is she still grieving for that man?" Dr Beria asked, in a sneering tone of voice. (This was a few weeks after Bob's death.)

"Yes, it's hardly surprising either. He had always been very kind to her, ever since she was little more than a child," replied Ratty.

As far back as September, 1991, Dr Beria had told Ratty that I was by far the most competent employee in his department. Also, he had told the Lady Mayoress, who had been visiting Barts, that I was the best secretary he had ever had.

During one of his many conversations with Ratty, Dr Beria turned from Jekyll to Hyde.

"Well, of course, we all expected her insane reaction to Maxwell's death. She was overtly disturbed when she heard the news. Her behaviour was not unlike that of your average mental patient," he said to Ratty the morning after Bob had died.

"I find your attitude repugnant," replied Ratty, "particularly in view of your words to the Lady Mayoress, namely that Eleanor was the best secretary you had ever had."

"That was then. This is now," said Dr Beria, adding, "You do know that she's been crossed off the books of most employment agencies, don't you?"

This was a reprobate lie, coming from the lips of a man, who had once praised me in such exaggerated terms.

I returned to work after my compassionate leave, but Dr Beria ignored me. When I had returned on occasions in the past, however, he had greeted me like a dog whose master had been away for months on end.

The only person who refrained from being icy and standoffish towards me was Julia, although she had prevented me from taking Friday afternoons off. I went out of my way to make friendly overtures to the other members of staff, but they were all anti-Maxwell and therefore anti-me.

Even my union rep, Simon Curruthers (name changed), turned against me, although I had paid all my union fees. He refused to support me because he, too, was anti-Maxwell. For reasons best known to himself, he wanted to meet my father. This could possibly have been because he was a fearful snob, even though he was a militant Left-winger.

The newspapers continued to be peppered with articles about Bob. Betty told me that her husband's mental state had deteriorated dramatically towards the end of his life. I had not been allowed to see him at that time. It was Betty, who had told me about the savagely unpleasant relationship between Bob and his father, which could have been a contributory factor to Bob's behaviour in later life. I have mentioned Bob's relationship with his father earlier.

I'm pleased I never witnessed Bob's emotional downfall. Apparently, he frequently flew into rages and sometimes even threw objects about.

To give an example of his behaviour, towards the end, a Russian Literature tutor from Sussex University, had translated some of Alexander Pushkin's poems into English. The tutor's name was Robin Milner-Gulland. He is dead now. He had a simpering and effete manner. I had disliked him intensely, because he was strongly averse to my love of black humour. He had disliked me as much as I had disliked him.

Most of his colleagues loathed him, because he had foul breath and was an infrequent bather. One of them, a certain Colin Bearne, referred to him as "Gullible Milland," and encouraged the students to call him that as well.

Gullible Milland made an appointment to see Bob, with a view to getting his book published. During the early part of the meeting, the namby-pamby tutor made the mistake of indulging in small talk, before offering his work to the peremptory publisher.

"You must know someone called 'Eleanor Berry'. She used to canvass for you, some years ago. It was in all the papers," ventured Gullible Milland.

"Yes," said Bob non-committally.

"I can't say I like her very much," remarked Gullible Milland, adding, "She has a most perverse sense of humour and is extremely eccentric, arrogant and aggressive."

Bob was at his very worst that day, partly because his thought processes had deteriorated, and partly due to his loyalty towards me. He shouted loudly at Gullible Milland in Russian and called him "Ti", the equivalent of "Tu" throughout his address. Gullible Milland had always been timid, retiring and cowardly. He was the kind of man that Bob would have despised, even if he hadn't been nearing the end of his life.

The language spoken during their brief conversation changed abruptly from Russian to English. Bob was unable to control his temper, because of Gullible Milland's timidity, as well as his negative attitude towards me. He observed the man's blackened teeth and his general unwashed state.

Her banged his fist on the desk. "You've got teeth like piano keys, you stink like a badger, and you look like the wreck of the fucking Hesperus!" he shouted.

"Am I to understand that you are not interested in publishing my translation of Pushkin's poems, Mr Maxwell?" asked Gullible Milland.

"Oh fuck off, you silly old tramp!" said Bob.

There was another incident during Bob's decline. Someone had brought a cheese omelette to his office on a tray. The sight of the omelette, although as yet untasted, did not appeal to Bob. He picked up the tray and threw it onto the floor.

There were other incidents during that period of his life which, on being witnessed, caused even crowded rooms to empty. His staff, and indeed the bankers who were involved in his finances, put as much distance between him and themselves, as they possibly could. The matter of the *Mirror* pension funds was lamentably tied up with his final illness. In other words, I genuinely can't see that he was personally responsible for what happened. His thinking faculties were no longer intact.

Bob's main illness was emphysema and the fact that he couldn't get enough air from his remaining lung to his brain. This had devastating effects on his circulation and, of course, on his heart.

There was yet another factor, contributing towards Bob's strange behaviour towards the end of his life. He had been hopelessly in love with one of his secretaries, a young woman called Annabella Williams, whom I have mentioned already. (I have changed her name.)

Annabella had light brown hair and wore short mini-skirts. Apart from these two things, there is really very little to say about her, except that she is well-spoken and has a good figure.

Bob had found out that she had been having an affair with a much younger man than he. His name was Nick Davies and he worked on the *Mirror*. Bob had been told that Annabella planned to marry Davies. I think he found out by bugging her phone. The *Mirror* proprietor shook convulsively, went berserk and asked someone to give him a glass of water. The fact that he had gone so far as to bug other people's phones, shows that he had completely lost it.

He desperately tried to dissuade Annabella from marrying Davies, to whom, in an endearingly child-like manner, he referred repeatedly as "that dreadful man." He wanted to marry her himself, despite their differences in age.

Bob failed to get his wish. Annabella married Nick Davies, and the older man suffered a broken heart.

I had many conversations with Betty after Bob's death, as well as during his life. At one time, she complained profusely about Annabella, and said that she was incapable of filing things properly.

"Oddly enough, I had a lot of trouble with that woman, as well." I said, adding, "I found her rude and intrusive, as well as being dressed like a common street woman all the time." I think Betty liked my remark.

I like to remember Bob for being kind, devastatingly attractive, outrageous and generous. I'm so glad I didn't see him towards the end of his life. I think I've said this before.

* * *

Let us stop referring to Bob, for the time being, and return to St Bartholomew's Hospital.

Nearly all the staff in the department appeared to despise me, except, of course, Julia. Rita Cassidy told me she could have done without my relatives ringing up our office, after Bob's death. I considered this to be a tactless and unattractive thing to say.

Rita also criticized me for drinking after hearing the sad news. Doris had probably told her that I had been the worse for wear later on that evening.

On my return to Bart's, I was asked to occupy the office on the ground floor and to help with the switchboard. The office was cold, unwelcoming and had no natural light. None of the secretaries spoke to me. However, I remained on friendly terms with a West-Indian girl called Margaret Samuels. She was the appointments manager in the department. She, too, hated Dr Beria. She told me that he was in the habit of stealing women's washing from clothes lines.

I felt wretched during my first day back at the hospital. Dr Beria came over to where I was sitting. He didn't smile. He didn't say "good morning," or even "hullo". He handed me a piece of paper, with a phone number written on it.

"Ring this number and get my son on the line," he commanded.

"Ring this number and get my son on the line, *what*?" I replied.

"Oh, I suppose I'll have to say 'please'," he said reluctantly.

I did as I was told but his son didn't answer.

"Come on, haven't you managed to reach my son, yet?" said Dr Beria impatiently.

"He's not answering his phone," I said coldly.

"Let me try," he said. "I'll find him far more quickly than you can!"

"Oh, please do," I said in a sarcastic tone of voice. I left the room.

I took the lift to the top floor, so that I could speak to Rita. I thought, perhaps, that she might have been more sympathetic towards me than the staff in the ground floor office had been.

"Hullo, Rita. We're friends, dammit! Why is everyone downstairs making me feel like a leper?"

Rita looked up from her computer and stared at me without smiling.

"Probably because they're all sorry for those poor *Mirror* pensioners. Aren't you sorry?" she asked. Her eyes were glacial.

"I've always felt much sorrier for the victims of bombs,

planted by those bloody fellow-countrymen of yours," I replied, adding, "Your friends even blew up some children who were visiting the Tower of London once!"

I left the office, slamming the door behind me. I felt like a South African black on a whites-only train. I reported Rita to Julia. I told her that the hospital had once been my second home and that I was terribly hurt by the fact that everyone had turned against me, including Dr Beria. Julia was pleasant and sympathetic.

"Go home," she said. "I'll have a word with Dr Beria."

"You're very kind," I said stiltedly.

Julia made me some tea.

"This will cheer you up. Why don't you go outside and get some fresh air? Then come back and we'll have a chat."

I returned to Julia's office in an even more paranoid state than before. "I know there's something going on in the department. Everyone is being so hostile towards me. It seems as if they all want to get rid of me," I said.

"You're talking like this because you're not well," said Julia. "No-one's trying to get rid of you. You're a very good worker. As for Dr Beria, I'm sure, he's not trying to get rid of you either. Why don't you go home? You'll feel much better in the morning."

That evening, I cheered myself up by having a few drinks at Ratty's house in Harley Street. I told Ratty what had been going on at the hospital that day. He poured me a double gin and tonic and filled up my glass when I had finished it.

Wolf Mankowitz, the American writer, was also in the house. Ratty introduced me to him. He had recently written a biography of Edgar Allan Poe and was a patient of Ratty's. He was sitting in front of an artificial log fire, drinking herbal tea. I turned to him.

"Sorry I'm drinking so much," I began apologetically, "I am the victim of a persecution campaign at my workplace. My persecutors resent the fact that I had been a close friend of the late Robert Maxwell's."

The American writer fixed me with a curious stare. There was something about him that I definitely didn't like. He asked Ratty for more herbal tea.

There was a long silence. He failed to reply to my friendly, if self-pitying overtures. I drank some more gin and became more spontaneous.

"Do you think Edgar Allan Poe ever practiced necrophilia?" I asked the writer, adding, "I have been strongly influenced by his poems *The Raven* and *Ulalume* which, as you know, are overtly preoccupied with themes of love and death."

I thought my question was quite intelligent, considering the amount of gin that I had consumed. The writer gave me an extremely hostile look, however.

"Lady, quit the bottle and get some therapy!" he replied rudely.

I was livid. "I don't go to America and insult Americans, so kindly don't come to my country and insult me!" I shouted, adding, "I have to go onto Prozac whenever your bloody fellow-countrymen are over here."

Poor old Ratty tried in vain to smooth things over between us.

I continued, "Incidentally, your biography of Edgar Allan Poe is not without flaws. I have read several biographies of him, many of which are superior to yours. For instance, unlike his other biographers, you have failed to tell your readers that he was a diabetic."

Mankowitz took another sip of his herbal tea. "I guess I slipped up there, Lady," he muttered apologetically.

I suddenly felt friendly towards him. "I enjoyed the passage in your book, describing young Poe throwing stones at his foster-father's house," I said.

"I guess that's exactly what he did do," said Mankowitz.

He and I were friends by the time I left that evening. Ratty was really relieved. He had always liked his patients to get on.

* * *

I returned to the hospital the following morning and went to the ground floor office, where I was told to help with the switchboards once more.

Very few calls were coming in that morning, so I took a thriller by James Hadley Chase, out of my bag. Its compulsively gripping pace took my mind off my misery.

Dr Beria came over.

"Oh, James Hadley Chase," he began, "My favourite of all his books is his first one, *No Orchids for Miss Blandish*. Since he died, a lot of writers have ghosted books in his name – at least, that's what I've heard."

I could tell that Dr Beria was making an effort to sound friendly, but everything about him seemed false. I knew Julia had been speaking to him.

"Someone told me that Kingsley Amis had ghosted quite a few of his books," I said.

Dr Beria turned off his charm, which it had been such a strain to muster. He walked out of the room.

Eventually, I was moved back to the office, which I had shared with Rita, the office in which I had heard about Bob's death, from my brother, Adrian. The sun was beaming through the window, cheering up the room.

"I'm sorry about what I said the other day, concerning the *Mirror* pensioners," said Rita. I thought that her behaviour had been unforgivable but I desperately needed an ally.

"That's all right, Rita," I forced myself to reply.

"I really didn't mean to hurt you. It just came out."

I cleaned my computer screen, turned the machine on and got it ready.

"All right, all right," I said. "I forgive you, as long as you don't mention *Mirror* pensioners to me again." Rita was still determined to continue the conversation.

"I don't understand why you were so upset," she said. "Maxwell wasn't even related to you." I tried to control my rage.

"Maxwell saved my fucking life," I began, "and did nothing other than show me kindness and goodwill. I don't want to discuss the subject any more. Try to remember, I am not made of iron. I am a human being. Besides, I've got a lot of work to do."

Two weeks passed. I was on fairly good terms with Rita once more. She, Doris and I went drinking after office hours every evening, but we didn't go to the pub I had disgraced myself in.

Once I had settled down in my old office, I became a new person, although I still missed Bob, and well remembered my last meeting with him, when he had shown me round the *Mirror*, holding my hand because he was afraid I would fall over.

I typed Dr Beria's tapes and made sure my letters were perfect. I visited other medical secretaries outside the department during tea breaks. They, too, hated Dr Beria, with whom they had had contact at some time or another.

Dr Beria continued to ignore me. If he wanted me to do a job for him, he made sure I was out of the office, so that he wouldn't have to speak to me. Sometimes, he left curt notes on my keyboard.

My dislike of him increased, but as long as I typed his letters perfectly, I thought there was nothing he could do to harm me.

My well-being was short-lived, however. It was eleven thirty a.m. on Friday, 14th February, 1992, St Valentine's Day.

While I was working, Dr Beria crept up behind me, startling me. I turned round and he gave me a false, almost toothless smile.

"May I have a word with you in my office, love?" he said. His voice was scarcely above a whisper.

I picked up my notebook, in case he wanted to dictate something and I went into his office. I had no idea what was happening, only the knowledge that Dr Beria was morbidly obsessed by me, and that my union rep, Simon Curruthers, was on his side.

As Dr Beria was the head of the department, and as I had no backing whatever, I knew that I would have to put up a heroic fight, if I were to win.

Dr Beria was not alone in his office. A senior representative from the Department of Human Resources, called Sheila McIlroy, was there as well. She was a tiny little doll of a woman. She was wearing pebble glasses and spoke with a heavy Liverpool accent.

She was sitting on Dr Beria's side of the desk, in order to intimidate me, but Bob's spirit burned within me. Also, I was wearing a locket containing his photograph.

I also remembered Ratty's account of Bob speaking to him from beyond the grave, when he had said, "Look after Eleanor". I knew that Bob was in Dr Beria's office, by my side and his presence gave me strength.

I sat down opposite the pair. "What's all this in aid of? What's the problem?" I asked aggressively.

"I'm very worried about you, Eleanor," said Dr Beria.

"Why?"

Dr Beria was lost for words and repeated himself.

"If you waste your time worrying about me, might I suggest that your other worries are somewhat remote," I said, looking at him defiantly. Why have you called me into your office?" I asked.

"Dr Beria's worried sick about you," said Sheila.

I raised my eyes to the ceiling, as if I were talking to a couple of fruitcakes.

"Why?" I repeated.

"Because he thinks you are mentally ill," said Sheila.

"I didn't know he was a psychiatrist," I said.

"He has formed this opinion, because you don't relate to people in an appropriate manner."

"To whom have I not related in an appropriate manner?" I asked. "Back up your statement with evidence. This rubbishy witch-hunt is a ludicrous waste of my time and the taxpayer's money. I've got a lot of work to do, and I would appreciate it if you would let me get on with it."

"One of the reasons I have called you in here, is that you are abnormal, in that you worship a man who is hated by the whole nation," commented Dr Beria.

"'*He was my friend, faithful and just to me,*' (Julius Caesar, Act III, Scene II)", I said, my voice raised.

"We are all familiar with Shakespeare's plays," said Dr Beria, "did you see in this man?"

"Do you mean Robert Maxwell?"

"Yes."

"There are many reasons why I thought so highly of him," I said. "He saved my bloody life. He invited me to stay in his house for a year, when I was thrown out of the Y.W.C.A. in Oxford."

"Were you thrown out of the Y.W.C.A for sexual reasons?" asked Dr Beria.

"No. Sorry to disappoint you."

"What else did this man do? What was so marvellous about him?"

He gave me moral support all the time. Particularly when there were printers' strikes on my father's newspapers. Living at my parents' house was intolerable. He gave me birthday presents. He helped me with my Russian…"

Dr Beria interrupted me. "You have been involved in a myriad of incidents and the smooth running of this department cannot be guaranteed while you remain in post." He took his glasses off and wiped them genteelly with his handkerchief.

"Are you trying to dismiss me, Dr Beria? I defy you to name one of these incidents," I demanded, my voice raised once more.

"I'm referring to your exhibitionist abuse of the tannoy system. When you speak over the tannoy, you sound like the bloody *Gestapo*, at the very best of times. You were put on tannoy duty a few weeks ago. You failed to realize that the tannoy is automatically broadcasted over some of the wards, where patients hover between life and death."

"Well I never!" I exclaimed, "You're talking as if I had said something indecent over the tannoy."

"It was far worse than that," said Dr Beria, "I was attending to a terminally ill patient, when I heard your booming voice. You were ranting with a Hitlerian rasp. Your exact words were, 'A dented, old, Polish Lada has been parked outside the mortuary. I have had disgusting language thrown at me, by five different firms of funeral directors. Would the owner of this car kindly remove as soon as possible'." Dr Beria continued. He made a poor attempt to imitate my voice. "The hearses are unable to gain access to the building to pick up the bodies.'"

"That heinous heap of metal belongs to you, Dr Beria. It was entirely your fault that the hearses couldn't get in!" I said.

"That's not the point. The word 'hearse' is never used in the hearing of seriously-ill patients. Also my car is neither dented, nor old. You were appallingly rude about it, and one simply doesn't refer to 'hearses' over the tannoy."

"Hearses exist, Dr Beria, and there are occasions when they have to be mentioned. Had you been considerate enough to park your ghastly old car on a meter, or in the hospital car park, this incident would never have occurred," I said. "Besides, my eardrums were almost perforated by the funeral directors' staff. Some of them used the foulest language. I had to ask them, 'Is this the kind of language you use, when you speak to the bereaved?'"

Dr Beria leant forwards, clasping his hands. He had no sense of humour whatever.

"Your words show that you are incapable of relating to people in an appropriate manner," he said.

"This is outrageous!" I shouted, "The hearses weren't able to pick the blasted bodies up, because your bloody car was in the way."

"You have a reputation for being eccentric throughout this hospital," said Sheila, veering away from the subject.

"OK, so I'm eccentric. Why shouldn't I be eccentric?" I asked aggressively. "I am an extremely hard worker. The fact that I'm eccentric is neither here nor there."

"The British don't tolerate eccentricity," said Sheila forcefully.

"*I am* British!" I shouted.

After a long silence, Dr Beria spoke once more. "I believe you're very unhappy," he said.

I rose to my feet and leant over his desk, pointing my index finger at Dr Beria. I stated: "I have served you for five years with loyalty and dedication. You told the Lady Mayoress that I was the best secretary you'd ever had. I have pandered to your requirements, such as making you tea, when the making of tea, whenever you want it, does not come into my job description.

"I have worked overtime almost every evening, to complete your letters to perfection." I continued, "Yes, I am unhappy. I am unhappy because I am hurt. In the past, you welcomed me back every time I had been on leave.

"'It's so nice to have you back', you used to say.

"This time, when I came back after bereavement leave, all you did was order me to get hold of your son, without even saying 'please'."

I noticed Dr Beria's hang-dog expression. He lowered his head, and his forehead almost touched his blotter. He blushed like a flighty débutante.

"I've never actually been rude to you, have I?" he asked pathetically.

"Not half as rude as you are to some of the nurses, who are too frightened to answer you back, but rude enough," I replied.

"When was I rude?"

"I walked past you in the corridor yesterday morning, and said, 'good morning, Dr Beria.' I didn't hear so much as a blessed murmur."

"I didn't hear you. Otherwise, I would have said 'good morning'."

"Also, you've been deliberately ignoring me. Outside in the square, you turn away from me and walk in the opposite direction, whenever you see me. You shirk contact with me all the time and you make it obvious that you don't want me to go on working here."

Again, the hang-dog expression and the blush.

"I called you in here because you are ill. I'm offering you another two weeks' sick leave," said Dr Beria.

I wish I'd accepted his offer but at the time, I thought it would be best to protect myself with an image of selfless industry.

"I'm not ill and I'm not taking two weeks off!" I persisted.

"You're ill in the head," he said. "Your reaction to Robert Maxwell's death was abnormal."

"I grieved for him, because he was such a lovely man. What abnormality lies in grief?"

Dr Beria suddenly looked as if a dentist's drill had hit a nerve. His jealousy of Bob was more than evident.

"When you were told that he was dead, you asked one of the consultants to go out and buy you a bottle of gin," he said.

"That's a bloody lie! You've tried to break my spirit but you have failed. If you dare to dismiss me, I will take you to court and sue you for unfair dismissal. I'll ruin you, Dr Beria!" I continued, "Incidentally, to dismiss me, you have to issue me with a certain number of warnings first. Not once, during my employment by this hospital, have I received so much as a single warning."

"We have ways of dealing with a case such as yours," said Sheila obscurely.

I wish I had made a tape recording of the interview. Dr Beria looked shattered, like a bull, having given up its desire to live.

"I've got to teach my students now," he said quietly. He sounded exhausted and looked at Sheila. "Will you take over from me, Sheila?" he asked feebly. He left the room.

"Don't worry, Dr Beria. I'll be able to handle her."

There was a silence which lasted for about five minutes.

"Did you have an affair with Robert Maxwell?" asked Sheila intrusively.

"That's none of your fucking business!" I shouted, but when

I realized I had used the F-word, I changed the wording of my reply, to save my skin.

"Sorry, I meant, that's none of your accursed business," I said.

Although Bob had never been my lover, I wanted Sheila to repeal my words to Dr Beria, so that the ambiguity of my statement would hurt him.

Suddenly, Sheila began to stare fixedly at my eyes. She did not avert her gaze for quite some time. Nobody has ever stared me out in my life. Even on trains, I have travelled way beyond my destination, to out-stare someone daring to stare at my eyes.

Sheila's eyes, which peered into mine from behind her pebble glasses, were small, bright blue and piercing. I was determined to stare her out, even if it meant my having to do so until it was time to go home. She finally backed down and her features broke into a bemused smile.

"What's going to happen to me now?" I asked.

"You will receive a letter, sometime next week, summoning you to a disciplinary hearing, in the offices of the Department of Human Resources," said Sheila.

"So, I'm to be disciplined because I preferred Robert Maxwell to Dr Beria, am I? This reminds me of King Henry II turning against his former friend, Thomas à Becket, for loving God more than he," I said.

"Not having heard of either of these people, I can't comment on your remark," she replied. Hadn't this mosquito-like woman gone to school? Hadn't she studied History?

Sheila buggered off, without saying "goodbye". She was wearing rather common, white, stiletto-heeled shoes, clacked like castanets. The sound which they made gradually decreased as she walked further and further away from Dr Beria's office, towards the lift.

* * *

A week passed and I heard nothing. I assumed that it was not thought to be against hospital regulations, to have been upset by Robert Maxwell's death. I thought I was in the clear.

I discussed the matter at length with my father, who very kindly offered to visit Dr Beria in his Harley Street consulting rooms, and tackle the demented doctor, face to face.

"My father intends to see you in your private rooms," I said to Dr Beria in the lift one morning. My tone was like that of a headmaster.

He whitened. "I don't want this to happen," he whined. He sounded like an anaemic boy.

A month later, when my happiness had almost returned, my office phone rang. The caller was Simon Curruthers, my union rep. (Throughout this narrative, I have changed his name, as I stated earlier.)

"Dr Beria has complained that relations between him and yourself have irretrievably broken down. He wants you to be transferred to another department," he said curtly. I could tell, by his voice, that Curruthers was as queer as a nine-bob note. I thought for a moment, he was on my side. He continued, "Old McIlroy was stamping up and down the corridor, in her bloody high heels, shouting, 'This has got to be discussed!'" I felt a note of sympathy in his voice but it was short-lived.

Dr Beria had engineered my move to the Department of Human Resources, where one person after another, was being made redundant, because of government cuts.

As he wished, Dr Beria could not actually have been charged with dismissing me unfairly, since he had merely had me transferred to another department.

When I was told I was being made redundant from the Department of Human Resources, I was given plenty of notice and a golden handshake.

On the day of my departure, my friends from other departments, including faithful Doris, came to my office to say "goodbye". They presented me with a bouquet of flowers and sang, "*For She's a Jolly Good Fellow.*" I made rather a feeble speech, in which I kept referring nonsensically "to the bleeding songs of Jarrow."

I went outside and sat down on one of the seats in the square. I was feeling very depressed.

"Hullo, Eleanor," My union rep, Simon Curruthers, sat down beside me.

"Hullo, Simon. You gave me absolutely no support whatever, although I had paid my union fees. I demand a refund. I'm upset because I've always liked this hospital," I said.

"You might like this hospital, but this hospital definitely does not like you," said Curruthers unpleasantly.

I was too stunned to comment on his words. Uncharacteristically, I lowered my head and said nothing. I knew that Bob would have bitterly disapproved of my behaviour, at that time.

"How do you feel at the moment?" Curruthers loved to offer someone the putter when their ball was in a bunker.

"I feel betrayed and very depressed," I replied.

"Don't you think the poor *Mirror* pensioners are feeling betrayed and very depressed? At least, you've got inherited wealth. They have not," said Curruthers.

I wanted to twist his cock off. Instead, I said, "You don't get any accolades for hitting women below the belt, Curruthers. You only make yourself look despicable, like the pimp that you are."

"I don't like crooks who call themselves socialists," he said.

"And I don't like brown-hatters.[16*] Incidentally, do you pitch or do you catch?" I asked.

"That was a very offensive question," said Curruthers. This time, I felt my grandfather, F. E. Smith's spirit burning within me. It was as if he had come back from beyond the grave, to help me to speak with his caustic tongue.

16* Brown-hatters: outmoded slang for homosexuals. The word is self-explanatory.

"It was provoked by a highly offensive remark," I said spontaneously. F. E. Smith and Bob were looking down on me, together. my depression dispersed temporarily.

Curruthers said nothing. He got up and went into the hospital. I walked towards the main gates. I hate being given flowers. On my way out, I threw them over the mortuary wall.

I hailed a taxi and asked to be taken to Harley Street. I called at Ratty's house. Co-incidentally, he had had a cancellation that afternoon.

"The bastards have thrown me out, Ratty," I said.

"Poor you! Let's go round the corner to the pub. You can have whatever you want. Everything will be on me."

"Thank you, Ratty."

I had just finished my first drink.

"I'm out of work now," I said. "Is there any chance of my working for you?"

"I don't see why not. My present assistant is leaving in September to get married. You're welcome to come aboard then. I desperately need a debt-collector and you've got the perfect voice for that. Why don't you take a holiday in the sun, in the meantime?"

"I'll go to Marseille, my favourite place. Thank you, Ratty."

"I'm sure you'll get on well with my wife. She's very young. Her name's Gida. She's black. We've got a son called Joshua − Joshua Amos, to be precise. He's eighteen months."

Before I went to Marseille, with my beloved Peaches, alas dead, I visited Barts to see Doris and take her out to lunch. It was late summer and Dr Beria had been sitting on one of the seats, in the square pathetically waiting for me. Somehow, he had found out I was having lunch with Doris. It's possible she had told him.

He bounded towards me. "Happy birthday, love!"

"What do you mean? My birthday is in May," I replied coldly.

"I was away in May," he said, "I've bought you a present."

He handed me an unwrapped bottle of *Coco Chanel*. I handed it back to him.

"Bob always preferred me to wear *Givenchy*," I said, in a cutting tone of voice.

"But he's dead."

"I don't regard him as being dead. Anyway, dead or alive, he was one hundred thousand times the man you are, or were, or ever could be." (This is a quotation from Thomas Hardy's "Far from the Madding Crowd.")

I ignored the tears in Dr Beria's eyes.

"Oh, love, will you ever forgive me?" he pleaded.

"No. I was born under the sign of the Bull," I replied, "Taureans don't forgive and they don't forget. I am not a cruel person. In fact, I have a very kind heart, but if someone crosses my path, I can be very, very nasty indeed. Goodbye, Dr Beria."

Because of Dr Beria's treachery, I was depressed for a long time, even when I started to work for Ratty in Harley Street. My motto has always been, "an eye for a tooth and a limb for an eye." I do not wish to state the extent to which I punished Dr Beria, or indeed whether I punished him at all. Perhaps, I did. Perhaps, I didn't.

Ratty did. His articulate words blasted the cowardly little doctor to pieces, at a crowded medical conference. This had been a particularly important event in Dr Beria's life, because he had planned to introduce a drug which had just come onto the market.

Ratty recognized him and approached him. "Hullo, Dr Beria," he said. "I'm afraid I've got some very unpleasant things to say to you."

"Please, don't get angry, Victor," pleaded Dr Beria.

Ratty ticked him off, using fairly forceful language. Dr Beria's tea cup shook in its saucer.

I had gained a hollow victory, but a victory nevertheless.

During his reprimand, Ratty had accused the doctor of "peremptorily sacking me, when I was grieving, of kicking a sick woman while she was bleeding in the gutter, and finally, of behaving in a caddish and despicable manner."

According to Ratty, Dr Beria dropped some of his slides. Others, he had put into the viewing machine upside down. He had bent over, as if about to be sick, had sunk to the floor, like a down-and-out and had burst into floods of uncontrollable tears.

Good old Ratty!

In short, Dr Beria was the vilest coward I have ever met in my life. I am sure Bob was watching him from above that day. I know just how much Bob would have despised him. He would also have loathed Curruthers's guts. He couldn't stand queens.

I believe strongly in revenge. If Sir Winston Churchill had walked away with his tail between his legs, the Germans would have won the War. I like to see justice being done. I wrote vehement letters, both to Dr Beria and to Curruthers. I didn't get any replies. I inherit from my maternal aunt, Eleanor Smith, the tendancy to write punitive letters on provocation.

* * *

Conclusion

There has been much speculation about the cause of Bob's death. One theory is that a *Mossad* agent got out of a launch, climbed onto *The Lady Ghislaine* and pushed him overboard. Why would a *Mossad* agent wish to kill a man, who had been so devoted to Judaism, in the latter part of his life?

Another equally silly suggestion was proposed, namely that a disgruntled crew member had pushed him into the water. Had he done that, he would have pushed himself out of a cushy job.

A third theory, expressed in some British newspapers, was that Bob had committed suicide because he considered suicide the ultimate form of cowardice. I have discussed this matter earlier on in this book. Bob would never have committed suicide. Besides, he was very vain and, were he to deliberately die by his own hand, he would have put on his best clothes, instead of falling into the sea half naked.

Also, drowning is a horribly painful death. Doesn't anyone know what it feels like when water has gone down the wrong way?

As I have stated earlier in this book, Bob was in the habit of going to the back of *The Lady Ghislaine*, within the small hours of the morning to contemplate the wash. He spent a considerable amount of time doing this. Also, he had a poor sense of balance, which worsened as he got older.

The railings at the back of the boat only came up to his thighs. When Ghislaine spoke on television the day after his death, they came up to her waist.

I personally think he had a massive heart attack, which must have occurred while he was either standing looking at the wash, or leaning over the railings. In any event, it would not have been at all surprising, were he to have over-balanced and fallen forwards into the water.

The reader will recall that I have mentioned the possibility of a massive heart attack earlier. It is also possible that he died of a broken heart because he had been crossed in love.

* * *

On another matter, I am proud to have been among the women, whom Bob found gutsy and feisty. He repeatedly told me that I was all of these things, not to mention "beautiful". One thing which saddens me, is the fact that, throughout his life, Bob expressed the wish to write a book about loneliness. Even a press release, dating as far back as 1969, stated that he suffered from loneliness.

A man can have an adoring wife and a loving family, can live in comfortable surroundings, be extremely well-off and still be crucified by loneliness. I have always wondered what had made Bob feel so lonely.

To this end, I arranged for an analysis of his handwriting to be performed. I have underlined certain phrases and points which could be relevant to his loneliness. I have used the present tense throughout. The essay, which refers to Bob as "the writer", reads as follows:-

The writer is an observant, intuitive, innately intellectual person, whose actions are very much dictated by his instincts.

He does not <u>appear to be someone who would allow himself to be co-erced or persuaded to act against his wishes.</u>

He is _proud, independent, aloof and somewhat autocratic. His social manner should manifest pose, self-confidence and a little egoism._

There is a certain dominant quality about him, and what appears to be _a deficiency of warmth in the way he relates to others._ He probably enjoys occupying the limelight and expounding his views.

Nevertheless, one senses a fragmented element within his personality – particularly where personal relationships are involved, as if he finds it difficult or distasteful to forge concrete bridges between himself and others.

The writer _appears to vacillate between despondency and optimism,_ the latter perhaps being the more pronounced trait.

The handwriting conveys the impression that the writer has experienced some sort of serious trauma at some period (possibly bereavement, illness or a shattering disappointment), the effect of which remains with him and at times, casts a weighty shadow upon him.

However, his resilience, tenacity and even stubbornness, propel him forward and his sporadic flashes of spontaneity are infectious.

He is neither a self-pitying man nor a particularly compassionate one. _There is an element of rigidity in the way in which he seems to hold tradition, propriety and self-discipline in esteem. He is of a highly critical disposition, prone to impatience, intolerance and inflexibility._

So far as it is possible to determine, his interests and aptitudes would perhaps be of a more cultural nature – conceivably with a bias towards the written or spoken word.

While he does not appear to be emotionally demonstrative or particularly sentimental, he does seem to be fond of children, as well as being dutiful and loyal towards those for whom he feels responsible.

He is possessive and acquisitive (with people and objects) and he is inclined towards selfishness and insensitivity.

It is not in his nature to pretend to be what he is not, nor would he necessarily even consider such an act – if by so doing it would make others happy. In many respects, therefore, one could describe him as being honest.

He should make a very good friend, but a cold, belittling and unforgiving enemy. His predictability fluctuates, as does his mood. He is a human being –

and an ambivalent one at that. He guards his privacy <u>and appears to impose rigid guidelines on himself and even more stringent guidelines on others.</u>

There is a certain dynamic quality about him.

He appears to hold "Eleanor" in esteem. (I had taken the sample from a book which Bob had very kindly given to me). The book was entitled *Malice in Wonderland.* I wonder what the graphologist meant when saying the above. It is noteworthy that Bob told my brother, Nicky, not once, but twice, that there had been occasions when he had seen himself in me.

I have studied this scholarly, but exceptionally verbose analysis of Bob's handwriting carefully. I will take things point-by-point, namely the parts that I have underlined and which I think could be germane to his loneliness:-

1. *"He does not appear to be someone who would allow himself to be co-erced or persuaded to act against his wishes."* This unnecessarily long sentence means simply that the man is a maverick and is stubborn. A stubborn person can easily make enemies. If one has too many enemies, one automatically becomes lonely.

2. *"He is proud, independent, aloof and somewhat autocratic... "* This sentence is self-explanatory. Aloofness and autocracy can invariably lead to loneliness.

3. *"There is a certain dominant quality about him, and what appears to be a deficiency of warmth in the way he relates to others."* Once more, this statement is self-explanatory. I am not prepared to say whether it is true or not. It is merely the graphologist's opinion. If the graphologist is correct and if there really is a deficiency of warmth in the way the writer relates to others, he would inevitably end up being lonely.

4. *"One nevertheless senses a fragmented element within his personality, particularly where personal relationships are involved, as if he finds it difficult or distasteful to forge concrete bridges between himself and others."* This implies that the man finds it hard to make friends

and form relationships. Once more, it is suggested that he suffers from loneliness, for this very reason.

5. "*The writer does appear to vacillate between despondency and optimism.*" Once more, the graphologist is being unnecessarily pompous. He means that the man loops up and down in spirits. He could have a manic-depressive or bi-polar tendency and hence be lonely, because manic-depression in itself is one of the greatest known causes of loneliness.

6. "*The handwriting conveys the impression that the writer experienced some sort of serious trauma at some period, (possibly bereavement, illness or a shattering disappointment), the effect of which remains with him and, at times, casts a weighty shadow.*" This is the most important statement of all. The graphologist does not know Bob personally, but refers to the effect that the Holocaust had on him and his original family.

   Bob is lonely because the memory of losing those dear to him and, in particular, his beloved mother, is too traumatic for him to bear, given the extreme cruelty of the Nazis. It is due to these most horrible losses, and events, that he has difficulty in forming relationships in later life. Again, we are reminded of his loneliness.

7. Later on, we read the words: "*He is of a highly critical disposition, is prone to impatience, intolerance and inflexibility.*" If the graphologist is correct, then Bob can be extremely difficult, particularly to work for. When we take the horrors of Nazism, which so grievously affected him, into consideration, who could be unsympathetic enough to blame him for having the above-mentioned faults? Even so, I would not have wished to work for him on a paid basis, only to canvass for him and to work for him voluntarily. (As I said earlier in this book, Bob offered me paid employment twice and I turned him down twice.)

8. "*While he does not appear to be emotionally demonstrative or particularly sentimental, he does seem to be fond of children, as well as being dutiful and loyal towards those for whom he feels responsible.*" This could

imply that Bob is fundamentally a decent person, who is dutiful, loyal and child-loving. The statement in question tells us nothing about his loneliness, however, unless lack of sentimentality could marginalize him from both his peers and his subordinates.

"*He is possessive and acquisitive (with people and objects) and he is inclined towards selfishness and insensitivity.*" This statement is self-explanatory. Whether it is true is a matter of opinion. If it is true, these shortcomings in themselves could cause him loneliness. A possessive, acquisitive, selfish and insensitive person could indeed turn out to be lonely in the end and find it hard to make friends easily. I have touched on this point earlier.

However, we must ask ourselves, was Robert Maxwell possessive, acquisitive, selfish and insensitive? He may have displayed some of these flaws in character at certain stages of his life, but I genuinely don't think these adjectives apply to his personality as a whole.

9. "*Like all of us, he has weaknesses and fears, but probably wouldn't wear them on his sleeve.*" This statement can be traced to a remark which Bob once passed to his son, Philip, "*Unlike you, I keep the vaults of my tortured inner chamber firmly locked.*"

His "tortured inner chamber," definitely relates to his memories of his experiences during the German occupation of Czechoslovakia.

Not only that, he is probably also referring to his abject poverty as a child, to the fact that, until the age of eight, he had no shoes, and could never forget the pang of cold and hunger. No wonder he became a socialist! There is also a suggestion that he tends to bottle things up, rather than to discuss them with others. Could this cause him to feel lonely? I think it could do so. I would also like to refer to his expressed attitude towards those who consult psychiatrists. "If you use that crutch, you won't walk."

10. "*He should make a very good friend, but a cold, belittling and unforgiving enemy.*" This statement implies that Bob could see no harm in a friend and no good in an enemy. I am reminded of my uncle, Freddie Birkenhead's biography of his father, F. E. Smith once more. My uncle describes his father in exactly the same way, regarding his choice of friends and enemies. Bob cannot forgive those who have slighted him. This in itself, could account for his reduced circle of friends. Without a large circle of friends, one can become very lonely.

11. "*His predictability fluctuates, as does his mood.*" The graphologist's words yet again, suggest that Bob's behaviour towards others could easily isolate him from them and therefore cause him loneliness. If Bob is unpredictable, he can inspire fear in others, and hence cause others to avoid him. It would seem, therefore, that he is phenomenally lonely most of the time.

12. "*He guards his privacy and appears to impose rigid guidelines on himself, and even more stringent ones on others.*" The graphologist is being verbose again. He is saying that Bob is a private person, who sets strict standards for himself and even stricter standards for other people.

If the above statement (12) is true, it's not surprising that he suffers from loneliness. According to the graphologist, Bob can be unreasonable and hence finds it hard to make friends. I am sure I have referred to this matter earlier.

Also of note, not mentioned in the handwriting analysis, is Bob's strange behaviour at his three birthday parties in June 1988.

I found out that the names of nearly all his guests had been taken from the telephone directory. Apart from his immediate family, none of his friends were present, apart from me and I had gatecrashed.

This extraordinarily eccentric and even disturbing behaviour is that of a truly lonely man.

I do not agree with everything the graphologist has said. I am merely recording his opinion. This is that Robert Maxwell suffered from loneliness, caused mainly by the fact that he was not the easiest man to get along with, loveable though he was.

Nick Davies, a journalist on the *Mirror* and Bob's rival in love, wrote a book about his boss and covered his deep depressions.

On a rainy Sunday afternoon, Bob, who was in bed with a cold, is alleged to have wanted to "jump out of a window to end it all."

Severe depression, though very unpleasant, is rarely a static condition. As is suggested by the graphologist, Bob frequently had mood-swings towards the end of his life. I too, thought he was bi-polar at that period.

I would like to quote a remark, made by Bob on television during his later life, "I am a very happy person." On this occasion, he was being economical with the truth. He was not making any references to the loneliness and mental torture which had plagued him for nearly all his life. When he made this remark, he was feeling reckless and unmindful of the famous Russian proverb, *"Happiness is not a horse. It cannot be harnessed."* In other words, his remark was uncharacteristically silly.

Bob definitely was not a happy man, particularly as he grew older. His beloved secretary, Annabella Williams (name changed). had turned him down. He was having trouble with his marriage, although I believe this to have been his fault and not Betty's.

Also, he had become very over-weight and he felt unwell for most of the time. He was jealous of nearly all Ghislaine's boyfriends. In short, he was perilously lonely as was implied by the graphologist. I could go on and on. I only regret the fact that he never wrote the book about loneliness, which he had planned to write ever since he was a young man.

Following Bob's death, I was naturally sorry about the *Mirror* pensioners affair. Why should anyone blame me, and use me as a scapegoat, though? I refer to such bastards as Simon Curruthers, Dr Beria, Rita Cassidy and many others.

To this day, I feel very bitter about having lost my job at Barts, when the *Mirror* pensioners affair was far from being my fault. It wasn't Bob's fault either, because his brain had ceased to function normally, through acute lack of oxygen, as I have already explained.

Bob had always treated me as a friend. I am proud and honoured by this fact, and will be both of these things, until the day I die. Since Bob's death, terrible things have been said about him, particularly in the gutter press, because the cowards who wrote about him knew that he was no longer around to hit them back.

Even the Judge, who presided over the trial of Bob's sons, Ian and Kevin, remarked emphatically that some of the gutter press's coverage about Bob had been "grossly offensive".

Bob was not the evil crook that he had been made out to be by his persecutors. They blackened his name for financial gain, and showed no regard for the psychological harm which they were inflicting on his widow and children.

The nation forgets all too easily that Bob only had two years' formal education and no training in accountancy. It is known that the Board of Trade published a "report" so called, in 1969. The "report" stated that Bob was "unfit to be at the stewardship of a publicly quoted company."

Had he intended to deceive anyone deliberately, why was he not arrested? Why was he not tried and imprisoned? The answer is that there was no evidence that he was either a fraud or a crook. In England, we are innocent until we have been proved guilty.

I do not profess to know anything about high finance, but any unbiased, fair individual, who knew anything about Bob, would state that he sometimes made hasty decisions in moments of blind optimism, and that he could be cavalier in his judgement.

I agree, he could be reckless, and the reason for my opinion has nothing to do with high finance. He allowed me to drive his beloved Ghislaine, having been told that I had recently smashed up a car.

Bob was child-like in many ways. Sometimes, the child-like part of his personality, prevailed over the Maxwell part. It could be said, therefore, that his personality was disordered, particularly towards the end of his life.

The *Mirror* pensioners affair, in particular, shows the disordered side of his personality, during his rapidly-progressing terminal illness and the lack of oxygen to his brain. This, I have discussed earlier.

We all tend to take oxygen for granted. When it is not properly supplied to the brain, the patient cannot and does not act rationally. Even Bob's speech was distorted towards the end of his life. To give an example of this, he often referred to monkeys as "minkeys", and to the sea as the "tea".

In the past, Bob had always paid back what he had borrowed and had done so with interest. He would not have deliberately taken money from the pensioners, without intending to return it. I'm sure it was a massive heart attack which prevented him from doing so. He was a brilliant gambler, and had he lived, he would no doubt have raised enough money to repay the pensioners, from what he had gained on the tables.

So far, I have not touched on the significance of the mismanagement of the *Mirror* pension funds. I have not yet mentioned the effects that the disaster had had on the pensioners, themselves.

It is true that I have been graced with inherited wealth, and I am fortunate indeed. However, because of the voluntary work I have done, and what I have seen on my world-wide travels, I know what poverty is like. I am certainly not a person who does not know how the other half lives.

I worked a thirty-five hour week in hospitals all over London for a number of years, and fequently disguised my accent. I spoke with a heavy Irish accent, to hide my roots.

"Oh, I do wish you'd stop speaking with that dotty Irish accent!" said my paternal aunt irritably, as she sat at an oak table, pouring tea from a Meissen tea-pot.

During the years when I worked from nine o'clock till five o'clock, I have met people from different creeds and walks of life. I have seen poverty and destitution all over the world, particularly in the back streets of Marseille, a city which I used to visit once a year with my beloved Peachey (now dead.)

Don't think I don't know what it is like to be deprived of a pension, at the end of an industrious life! I defy anyone to tackle me, by saying that I am indifferent to the perils of being pensionless. It simply isn't true, and I refuse to be blamed for what happened, as I was at Barts.

On a lighter note, I can give an example of the behaviour of one particular *Mirror* pensioner. I was puzzled by the reference to this person in *The Evening Standard*'s *"Londoners Diary"* column.

The pensioner had complained bitterly that he could no longer afford to heat his swimming pool, at his holiday home in the south of France. When Bob was a child, he didn't know what a swimming pool was, heated or otherwise. The only bathing facility available to him, was a polluted river, which was bitterly cold, even during the summer months.

I rang up several newspapers to complain about the spoiled individual, who had said he had problems with the heating of his swimming pool. Among the newspapers I phoned was *The Evening Standard* itself.

My call to *The Evening Standard* was answered by a certain Anthony Cheeswright, a friend of my late brother, Adrian's. He was the model for Simon Farr, the hero of two of Adrian's early books.

Before I discovered Cheeswright's identity, I got particularly excited and spoke to him at length about the pensioner who had been unable to heat his blasted swimming pool.

"Oh, God, is that you, again, Eleanor?" asked Cheeswright.

***

I had been quite neurotic in the past, because of my justified suspicions that I was not valued for who I was as a person. Some people have seen me as an "affluent newspaper magnate's daughter" and, even worse, a "spoilt little rich girl."

Young men pursued me in my teens, to gain an introduction to my father, hoping to get jobs on his two newspapers, through the "old boy network". Countless individuals have despised me for having hailed from a Tory family and have taken unfair advantage of me.

The words, "You're lucky you're able to *afford* to take me out to dinner," have all too often been thrown in my face. Even the obnoxious Dr Beria had remarked, "Oh, well, rich people don't have feelings." He had uttered these words in a phone call with Ratty.

However, Bob, whose childhood had been about as destitute as any child's could have been, had given me every inch of his bear-like love, and had told me that he had valued me for what I was as a person. He had said this on many occasions. That is why I won't hear a word against him.

In July 1979, at the wedding reception for Bob's daughter, Christine, a cruel, odious, Left-wing politician lammed into me, unprovoked.

He was Peter Shore, who is dead now, thank God! He died of cancer. I wouldn't even have visited him, to spit on his morphine drip. He had been allocated a life peerage in 1997, long after his offensive behaviour towards me.

He was known as "The Right Hon. Lord Shore of Stepney". Fancy a man accepting a title like that, when he clearly despised those with titles.

Among other things, he had been the Labour MP for Stepney from 1964 to 1974 and Secretary of State for Economic Affairs from 1967 to 1969.

Peter Shore looked more like an ugly, mangy, floppy old dog, bundled in from outer space, than a human being. I have no idea why this freak had been sitting at Bob's side, as if he had been a welcome wedding guest. I put my hand on Bob's shoulder to tell him I was leaving.

Bob inadvertently introduced me to Shore in front of a microphone. His words could be heard by about two hundred people, as could Shore's reply.

Bob told the puzzled, befuddled creep about my achievements, namely my having taught myself Russian, my having joined the Communist Party and my having gone to Russia alone. Unfortunately, he told him about my father's trade, as an addendum.

"Oh, come on, Bob," said the Repulsive Piece Of, "You can do better than to introduce me to the daughter of an absolute shit like that!"

I couldn't have used violence towards Shore, in front of Bob, although I wanted to slap his face. I sneered at him, as disagreeably as I could and mouthed the words, "You'll hear from me again!" I'm pleased to say that he recognized the hostile expression on my face. I was so livid, that I decided to punish him, and punish him I did. I will not share the manner in which I punished him because I am afraid of losing friends.

I am not vicious or vindictive, unless I have been provoked. However, I hold burning and vehement views about the necessity of loyalty towards loved ones. I take inordinate trouble to ensure that those who have provoked me, by speaking ill of those dear to me, such as my beloved father, are punished. My attitude towards Peter Shore was the same as that towards Dr Beria,

Some say, "turn the other cheek," but I believe in revenge when it is deserved as I have said earlier. Had Sir Winston Churchill not believed in revenge, we would now be living under Hitler's and Eva Braun's grandchildren.

My father had been publicly dishonoured. Only an appropriate form of revenge, was good enough to punish that bastard, Shore.

I am proud of doing what I did to him, although what I did was absolutely horrendous. I only told old woman, Rohde (the psychiatrist) what I had done. The imbecile had responded by saying, in his characteristically high-pitched voice, "I think that's absolutely nauseating!" He had always been judgemental towards me. A psychiatrist is not supposed to be judgemental towards his patients. That's why I added Dr Jones to my repetoire.

As I said earlier, I was born under the sign of the Bull. When the spikes are driven into my shoulders, I don't back away and slump in the dust. Bob taught me not to do that. I go for the matador's stomach and I do not give up until his heart, lungs, liver and intestines are spattered over the ring.

My maternal aunt, the famous writer and self-confessed gypsy, Eleanor Smith, felt the same way as I do about revenge. I have mentioned my aunt before. Unfortunately, I never met her, as she died before I was born. The honour of loved ones was paramount to her and she fought tooth and nail to defend it.

I enjoy inflicting pain on sadists, because I know I am protecting vulnerable parties and preventing them from being at the receiving end of cruelty.

I would like to quote a remark made by the Russian writer, Nikolai Gogol. He made the following statement, while he was writing his story, *The Overcoat*. The quotation reads as follows:-
"How much inhumanity there is in man, how much savage brutality lies hidden, under refined, cultured politeness, and even in men whom the world accepts as gentlemen."

Those words were written for your benefit, the Right Hon. Lord Shore of Stepney. I bet that bastard was guilty of false, *"refined, cultured politeness,"* hiding savage brutality underneath it.

Incidentally, after Bob died, Shore was the first to turn against him, after having consumed his food and wine.

* * *

I have re-read Nick Davies's book, which was published shortly after Bob's death. Davies was Bob's rival in love, as I said earlier. He had married Annabella Williams (name changed), by whom Bob had been besotted. I do not propose to analyse the whole of Davies's book. However, he stated that Bob's children virtually trembled at meals, whenever their father was present. I can disprove Davies's statement and will do so.

I had lived at Headington Hill Hall for at least a year. On one occasion, Isabel had said, "Do you have to be so awful, Daddy? I don't know anything about Russian literature, do I?"

Isabel's remark was prompted by her father's complaint that she had pronounced the name of a Russian writer incorrectly.

Also, Ghislaine had once threatened to pour a bowl of strawberries over her father's head, because he had said that her dress was indecent.

Further, Kevin was not afraid of calling across the table to his father, "Is the honourable Member for Buckingham still capable of rising?"

I could go on indefinitely.

Bob was a born-again religionist who took his beliefs seriously. Would such a man have deliberately ruined other people's lives? Many financiers who worked for the *Mirror,* were totally corrupt, as were the bankers who were connected to the pension funds.

I suspect that they, and not a man with an oxygen-deprived brain, were guilty of what had happened. There again, high finance, like engineering, is a subject I know nothing about.

In this book, I have only sought to examine Robert Maxwell's character, personality and loving friendship with me, be it a platonic one. As far as I am concerned, he was a lovely, lovely man and a great big sweetie.

Further, the memory of his widow, Betty, who had been exceptionally kind to me over so many years, is something I shall cherish until I am laid in earth.

Now for some humorous anecdotes:-

INDEX OF ANECDOTES ABOUT ROBERT MAXWELL

ANECDOTES

Robert Maxwell and a Disgruntled Yorkshireman

I went into Bob's study one morning, during one of his Election campaigns. A man was with him. I knew who the man was, but I didn't like the look of him, so I avoided opening a conversation with him. I'll hand it to him that he wasn't responsible for his looks. Even so, I definitely did not wish to speak to him.

Bob pointed at him abruptly, using his thumb, "Do you know who this man is?" he asked rather disdainfully.

The atmosphere in the room made me rather nervous, so I raised my voice, as I always do when I am nervous.

"I haven't the faintest idea who he is. Does he work in your garden?" I replied.

"She doesn't mean to be offensive," said Bob. "She's just a bit shy."

The man was irritated and spoke with a heavy Yorkshire accent.

"Shoy? Shoy? Bluddy abroopt. I'd say!"

It was Arthur Scargill.

The Weird Parson and the Chicken

It was a Thursday, in late November, 1991, about three weeks after Bob's death. I was in London and I went out to lunch at my local restaurant. A rare ray of sun for the time of year, shone through the window I was sitting by. It was warming the right side of my face.

I was pleased to see that the restaurant was empty, because I wanted to be alone, savouring the sun and my memories of Bob.

An abnormally thin parson came into the restaurant. His face was unhealthily pale, his lips were moist and he had pale, watery, blue eyes. He had a leering, lascivious look about him, which disquieted me, even from a distance.

He came to my table and looked at me, as if he were assessing a ten bob knock. He sat down opposite me and continued to stare. I noticed that his hair was parted half way down his head to hide his baldness. I can't stand men who do part their hair in that manner.

"You don't mind if I sit here, do you?" he asked. He had a hearty, P.G. Wodehouse accent which sounded extremely common.

"Yes, I mind very much. All the tables in here are unoccupied, except this one. There are plenty of other places where you can sit," I replied.

He ignored my words and looked me in the eye for a while.

His eye contact was intrusive and a trifle chilling. He reminded me of Sheila McIlroy.

"How dare you stare at my eyes like that!" I said. He looked away.

A mini-skirted waitress, aged about twenty, came over to us.

"What will you have, madam?" she asked.

"I'll have a breast of chicken, grilled tomatoes and a double Gordon's gin and tonic. Would you please put the gin into a glass, with some ice and leave the tonic water in a bottle."

"Yes, madam, and you, sir?" asked the waitress.

"Dover sole, chips, peas and half a pint of lager, please," said the parson. He ogled the waitress's thighs.

The food was brought to the table. I thought about Bob once more. As I have indicated before, he had rather bestial table manners. I also felt strongly, once more, that the dead can sometimes see the living, if they had actually known the living.

I picked up the chicken breast in my hand, as Bob sometimes did, stretched across the table and dipped it into a bowl of sauce. I bit into it and wiped my mouth with the back of my hand. I drained the gin and tonic.

"I must say, I don't think very much of your table manners, young lady!" exclaimed the parson.

"How the hell do you think St John the Baptist ate his chicken in the wilderness?" I replied. I know that Bob had witnessed the scene and I could almost hear him laughing.

The Sotheby's Auction of Robert Maxwell's Possessions – see the central panel of "The Haywagon" by Hieronymus Bosch

I have mentioned this painting because it depicts men and women dipping greedily into sacks of grain. These represent gold.

The auction room at Sotherby's on a bleak February afternoon in 1992, was a cesspit of gluttonous, gloating riff-raff. Hate-filled hooligans lurched, like unfed vultures to get a closer view of the degradation of a dead man, who was unable to defend himself or to protect his property.

These rabid wolves jostled against each other, like cannibals and necrophiles, trying to sink their rotting teeth into a dead body, before violating it.

I was delighted to be there, because my presence proved that I am not a coward. I felt like a saint, overlooking an ocean of sickening, moral decomposition. I almost felt Messiah-like, as I trampled through this sea of utterly amoral felons.

"Let me through!" I shouted, "I knew the man. You did not!" I am proud to say that my words were quoted in *The Investors' Chronicle* (the February 1992 edition). Part of an article in the magazine read as follows:-

"A pretty, blonde woman, brandishing a (forbidden) cigarette, forced her way to the front, barking, 'Let me through! I knew the man. You did not! – A cry which some might have considered a trifle unwise, given the number of 'Mirror' pensioners in the crowd."

Unfortunately, the author of the article, did not know my name. I wanted to recite the whole of the "*O pardon me, thou bleeding piece of earth*" speech from *Julius Caesar*, at the top of my voice, in order to provoke a truly sickening audience.

Sick jokes were cracked by the callous carrion crow, wielding the hammer, his piteous humour blacker even than a demon's soul. He inspired sneering laughter from the leering ghouls, who appeared to be carnally roused by the prospect of a dead man being done down.

The scene reminded me of Nazis, attending a Nuremberg rally to hear Hitler's rantings. Bob was a devout follower of Judaism. It is said that anti-Semitism no longer exists in England. Perhaps it is not seen in living rooms. Take a look at the murals in North London, which blatantly display the foul level of anti-Semitism within the Labour Party. These were put up by orders of that bastard, Jeremy Corbyn. Anti-Semitism *does* exist in England and it *must* be stamped out.

Before I finish writing this anecdote, I stress that I am not blaming the *Mirror* pensioners, some of whom were said to be among the crowd that depressing February afternoon. I am blaming the other occupants of the crowd who nauseated me beyond oblivion.

A certain Gerald Jacobs, who was writing for *The Jewish Chronicle*, at the time, read my article. He commented, a trifle inappropriately, I thought, "*Eleanor Berry certainly does have an intense style of writing*"

I thought about his observation several times and, in the end, I had to laugh a little.

Finally, when *The Investors' Chronicle* stated that there had actually been *Mirror* pensioners among the crowd, there was no evidence that any of them were present. Given their accidentally caused circumstances, they would probably have lynched me, when I barked the words, "Let me through... etc." Hence, *The Investors' Chronicle* too, was taking the piss.

Stormy Elevenses with Maxwell and Proust

I have a phobia about illness, particularly in the case of those close to me.

It was a Saturday morning in the mid 1970s. Bob and I were having elevenses in the offices of *Pergamon Press*. We were drinking coffee.

"You don't need all that sugar in your coffee," he said. I ignored him. "Another thing, take your spoon out of your cup, when you've finished stirring your coffee."

We were talking about Proust's interminable work, À *La Recherche du Temps Perdu*, which I had once discussed with Betty. Bob was just as argumentative about the deathly prose, that I had been studying at university, as he had been about the coffee.

I became heated about Proust's dreary protagonist, Marcel, his obsession about his bedside light, and his tedious preoccupation with memories evoked by a crappy old biscuit.

"The bedside light may not have meant anything to you, but it meant a hell of a lot to the boy," said Bob.

I ignored his remark. I continued, "What really irritated me was the boy's habit of sending messages to his mother's cook, only to find out whether or not she would be coming to see him, to prove her love for him.

"What does it matter whether she loves him or not? Surely,

the boy's only logical motive for sending the messages, would have been prompted by his fear that his mother had been *taken ill.*"

"Why did you say that?" asked Bob. He leaned back in his chair and cleared his throat loudly. He always sounded like a gang of *Hell's Angels*, trying to start their motorbikes, whenever he did this.

"It's simple, Bob. It stands to reason. A boy wouldn't care whether or not his mother loved him. He would only be concerned about her imminent death," I said. I added, "The sole thing going through his mind would be a horrific fear, not of rejection but of bereavement."

He cleared his throat once more, and tilted his head backwards, as was his wont, when he was in an argumentative mood.

"Oh bollocks!" said Bob.

Robert Maxwell, The Irishman and the Bottle of Wine.

Miss Berry's publisher regrets that this anecdote is indecent and cannot be printed in full. It concerns a perverse Irishman.

Bob dared me to drink an entire bottle of red wine, at a birthday lunch, which he and Betty were very kindly giving me in early May, 1973. I drank it. Then he dared me to stand up and make a speech. Because he had caused me to become so inebriated, the speech I made was of a disinhibted and singularly disgusting nature.

Maxwell rang a bell. He had turned green and started to sweat heavily. There was a mild tremor in his hands.

Oping, a Filipino lady, who had worked for the Maxwells for a considerably long time, about fifteen years, scurried into the diningroom.

"You rang, Mr Maxwell" she said.

Bob clutched the dining-room table and rose to his feet.

"Mr Maxwell, are you all right?"

Bob didn't answer.

"Mr Maxwell, do you need help?"

"Yes. I am going to my room, where I wish to be given some hot, sweet tea," he said ponderously.

In hindsight, the whole episode was in fact Bob's fault, not mine. It was he who had dared me to drink the wine.

Incidentally, he personally had brought the bottle up from

the wine cellar, just before lunch. Having consumed it, egged on by my somewhat mischievous host, I could not possibly have been rightfully blamed, for having made such a revolting speech which I would never have dared to make, had I been sober.

Poor Old Mr Mutton

Bob, Betty, Jean and I were sitting in the study at the Wharf House, during the Election campaign in the summer of 1970. It was about nine o'clock in the evening.

A man called Joe Mutton had been working for Bob. He was very devout and spent some of his time in the Labour Party Headquarters and the rest of his time going to church. Sometimes, he canvassed for Bob but not very often.

Mutton rang Bob up continuously and insisted that he enter religious themes into his speeches. The frequency of these calls, together with their subject matter, irritated Bob who was watching a football match, having claimed that this was the only relaxation he could get. West Germany were playing Czechoslovakia.

Jean took the call. Mutton asked to speak to Bob urgently.

"Call for you from Mr Mutton, Mr Maxwell," she said, "He says it's important."

Bob was incensed because he had been interrupted while watching the football match. West Germany had just scored another goal and were winning. This did not improve his mood.

He told Jean to ask Mutton to ring again the following morning. However, Mutton insisted on speaking to him.

Bob lumbered across the room and took the receiver from Jean's hand. He was watching the television out of the corner of his eye. Czechoslovakia had lost yet another goal.

"Yes?" barked Bob.

Mutton was disturbed by Bob's abrupt telephone manner. He began to waffle inconcisely and referred to the alleged necessity of religious themes in his boss's speeches.

"Oh, by the way, it's Mutton here," he said eventually.

"B-a-a-a-a!" shouted Bob.

He hung up and returned to the game. The fact that Czechoslovakia was losing, had irritated him even more.

"What did he want, Papa?" asked Betty.

"That man, Mutton, is a Jesus glutton," said Bob.

Robert Maxwell Wins Challenging Battle to get Me
Out of Bed in the Mornings.

I lived at Headington Hill Hall for about a year after I had been thrown out of the YWCA, for reasons I gave earlier. For a man with such a short fuse, Bob bore my difficult habits stoically and patiently.

During the General Election campaign of early 1974, several people, including Bob and Betty, moved into the Wharf House. The house overlooked a stagnant canal and was near the Labour Party's Headquarters. (I'm sure I've said this before.)

At first, I was not that industrious and spent the mornings in bed, sleeping. Occasionally, I was stirred by the sound of vigilant campaigners, calling out the words, "Vote while you can. Maxwell's your man!" over loudhailers.

The Maxwells' had an Irish cleaning woman. I think her name was Mrs Mock. I was unaware at the time that Bob spent the mornings in the Wharf House. One morning, I was rumbled. From eight o'clock onwards, I was woken at fifteen minute intervals, by Mrs Mock's shrill Irish voice.

"Mr Maxwell says it's high time you were hopping out of your bed. He thinks you've been there quite long enough."

I ignored her visits. At twelve-thirty, the great man himself rattled into the room. He came up to my bed and sat on his haunches, like a policeman, asking a motorist whether he had

243

been drinking. He leant forward, his face less than a foot away from mine. I was struck by the extreme sweetness of his breath. He pointed vehemently, first at me and then at the ceiling. For some reason, I suddenly thought of the film, *A Clockwork Orange*, which I had seen several times. A quotation from it came into my head,

"*Leave us be and I'll be right as dodgers for this after!*" Bob seemed irritated.

"You! Up!" he shouted.

I knew the game was up for me. I obeyed him. After that, he made me sleep on a camp bed in his study.

This was not unpleasant, however. I woke up early every morning, because the bed was so narrow.

I watched Bob working at his desk, sitting in profile, without his knowledge. He often wore his tie loosened at the neck and the top two buttons of his shirt undone. This was something which set my blood on fire! I enjoyed lying there, looking at him, and what excited me most was the fact that he had no idea he was being watched.

The experience was similar to the thrill of a nature expert observing a fierce, wild animal, which thinks it is alone.

"A Truly Terrifying Human Being"

I was doing my A-Levels, during the year the Maxwells very kindly said I could stay in their house, rent-free.

Sometimes, after dinner, Bob gave me some secretarial work to do. This was easy because all his letters were short, although he dictated quite fast and I couldn't keep up with him.

"For Christ's sake, slow down, Bob!" I shouted.

He waited for about half a minute. He looked excited, puzzled and startled at the same time. He looked me in the eye, smiled strangely and tilted his head backwards, in his I Don't Know Whether I am Angry or Turned On pose.

"Are you all right, Bob?" I asked.

He stared into space as he spoke.

"I think others have told you this before," he said.

"Told me what?"

"You are, without doubt, a truly terrifying human being!"

"Come now, Bob, surely not," I said.

I shall never forget his words. They have haunted me to this day. Whenever I meet a man I find attractive, I try to treat him like Dresden china.

Robert Maxwell, President Nixon, and the "Pravda" Editorial

I was still staying with the Maxwells'. I was reading English at university at the time. (I got a 2:2.)

President Nixon and Watergate were dominating the newspapers.

After breakfast, one Saturday morning, Bob suggested that he and I read *Pravda* together. *Pravda* is a Russian newspaper and is the mouthpiece of the Communist Party elite. *Pravda* is the Russian word for "Truth". I had no idea where Bob had obtained a copy of the paper or, indeed, how he knew that the author of its interminable editorials, was being paid ten roubles a word.

The editorial, which Bob and I read together, was verbose, repetitive and monotonous. It said roughly the same thing over and over again, obviously so that its author could continue to earn his ten roubles a word. So terrified was the Soviet Government, led by Leonid Breshnev, of Nixon's apparent insanity, that *Pravda's* lengthy editorial ended this way, in bold capitals:-

PRAVDA THINKS THAT THE AMERICAN PEOPLE ARE BEING VERY RUDE AND VERY UNKIND TO THEIR BELOVED PRESIDENT!

Bob was in high spirits that day and let out his characteristic, guttural Cossack's laugh. His laughter was infectious.

Robert Maxwell and the Typhoid Injection

I had been taking 60mg of *Diazepam* (*Valium*) every night to help me to sleep over a long period of time. Suddenly, one of my doctors refused to give me any more, and the withdrawal symptoms were horrendous.

I had been invited to Headington Hill Hall for the day. It was Saturday, 28th July, 1983, when my sister, Harriet's youngest son was born. He is known as "Mingo" (short for "Domingo".) The weather was stifling and, because of my terrible cold turkey, I felt very ill.

Betty suggested that she and I walk up the hill to the offices of Pergamon Press to tell Bob lunch was ready. His mode of greeting me was as friendly as ever. Also, he was wearing his tie loosened at the neck, which set me blood on fire once more. I felt the same way as I had felt when my father had sent me, to Headington Hill Hall, to ask Bob for five thousand pounds towards the anti-airport fund.

I lost consciousness. When I came round, I failed to recognize either Bob or Betty. When a fainter regains consciousness, he loses his memory and is nauseated and frightened.

I was lying on the freshly-mown grass, just outside the offices of Pergamon Press. Bob was kneeling on the grass beside me, shaking me by the shoulders. Because I was lying down and he was kneeling by my side, I assumed at first that he was a doctor, possibly Dr Goldman. The two men didn't look alike but were equally as attractive.

I rolled up my sleeve and asked Bob to give me a typhoid injection. I failed to realize that he wasn't holding a syringe.

It soon became apparent to me where I was and who I was with, however. Apart from my severe anxiety, I was mortified with embarrassment.

Bob continued to kneel on the grass. He leant right over me, to make sure I was breathing, his lips about six inches away from mine. I noticed the sweetness of his breath once more.

"You're ill!" he said confrontationally.

"No, I'm not, Bob," I lied.

"I've seen you do this before, haven't I?"

"Yes, I think you have."

Bob got to his feet and brushed the blades of grass off his trousers. "I have two questions to ask you. First, what are you taking? Second, who's giving it to you?"

"I don't take drugs," I replied.

"I'm extremely concerned about the kind of company you are keeping in London," he said obscurely.

"The Rage of Marjorie Proops"

After Bob's death, there was prurient speculation about women going to bed with him. I read about this in the newspapers and it caused me agonizing jealousy. Also, I suffer severely from O.C.D – obsessive compulsive disorder which I inherit from my mother. I found out that Bob frequently addressed Mrs Marjorie Proops, the *Mirror*'s agony aunt as "my darling little daughter".

I couldn't really imagine him taking this strange-looking woman to his bed, but my obsession was such that I was prepared to believe anything. A demon got into me and prompted me to ring Mrs Proops at the *Mirror*. It was not difficult to find her.

Her voice was quite plummy. Her brogue could have related to one of many London accents. Her initial telephone manner was fairly unfriendly. I came straight to the point. I said, "Mrs Proops, I must know, when Robert Maxwell kissed you, was it on the cheek or on the mouth?"

"Who in the world are you?" she asked aggressively.

I said, "I'm not being rude but I am possessed. I suffer from obsessive compulsive disorder. I *must* know."

"You *are* being rude. Bloody rude! What do you want? Robert Maxwell was a very affectionate man," said Mrs Proops.

My obsession was causing me to suffer unendurably.

"When you say he was an 'affectionate man', does that mean he used to beckon you into a dark corner, and put his hand between your legs?" I asked, adding, "Did he put his hand under your bra? Did you have sex with him?"

The Agony Aunt blew a gasket. "Your behaviour is absolutely outrageous!' she bellowed. She hung up.

This didn't prevent me from ringing her back, and asking her the same questions. She was a brittle old bag. She threatened to call the police and have all my calls traced.

"Welcome to my bath."

I was doing a translation job for a firm in Oxford in the early nineteen seventies. The hours were 8:30 a.m. to 5:30 p.m. For a short period, I shared a flat with an extremely selfish woman, who prevented me from using the bathroom, between seven o'clock and nine o'clock in the morning. Her personal appearance was scrawny and, for want of better words, shrimp-like.

She was the daughter of a notorious public figure. I won't give his name. Quite apart from that, I don't know how to spell it. Apparently, the woman's father had had a murky criminal record, involving under-age boys.

I explained the bathing situation to Bob. He and Betty very kindly allowed me to use one of the bathrooms in their house every weekday morning. I was given permission to use Bob's private, majestic bathroom. It was a fantastic room. It would have made Cleopatra's bathroom, seem like that of a slum-dweller in Calcutta, in comparison.

It was almost seven o'clock on a cold, foggy morning in November. I had begun to dislike my job, because I wasn't allowed, either to use the phone, or to receive phone calls.

While I was driving to Headington Hill Hall, I developed a terrific hangover. I had slept badly the night before, because the woman I shared the flat with, had blared a transistor radio for most of the night. I threw a boot at it but it missed.

When I got out of my car, and started to walk towards the house, I had become even more groggy and disorientated than I had been when I started my journey.

I was rather surprised to see Bob leaving his house so early, and because I was barely awake, I made the following utterly fatuous remark, "Hullo! Fancy seeing you here!"

"I live here, don't I," said Bob.

THE END

The street in which Robert Maxwell was born on 10th June 1923

Robert Maxwell's house in Oxford (Headington Hill Hall).

Robert Maxwell's grave on the Mount of Olives in Jerusalem.
The author visited the grave in 2018.

The Lady Ghislaine – the yacht from which Robert Maxwell fell. The author assumes that he had sustained a massive heart attack. There is also the possibility that he died of a broken heart.

Robert Maxwell in front of a tank during World War II

Robert Maxwell as a toddler in Czechoslovakia

Robert Maxwell's mother, Hannah Hoch.
She died in Auschwitz.

Robert Maxwell being awarded the M.C. for bravery on the Field.
Field Marshall Montgomery is pinning the medal to his chest.

Robert Maxwell playing cards with patients,
after he had had a lung removed.

Robert Maxwell's photograph when canvassing during
the 1970 Election Campaign – aged 47.

Robert Maxwell as a young man

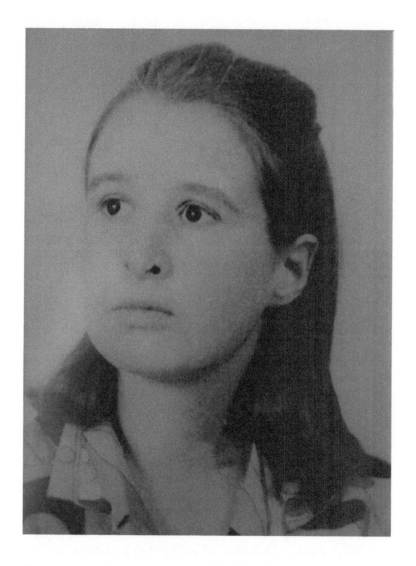

Eleanor during her teens, when she first met Robert Maxwell at his house in Oxford, Headington Hill Hall.

Eleanor and Jean Baddeley – known as "Bath Rota Baddeley",
Robert Maxwell's P.A. This photograph was taken by a *Daily Mirror*
photographer. Very sadly, Jean died before Eleanor completed this book.

Eleanor's mother, Pam Berry (later to become Lady Hartwell).
She and Robert Maxwell had a somewhat stormy relationship.

Eleanor's father, Michael Berry (later to become Lord Hartwell).
He was given a life peerage under Harold Wilson's Labour government.
There was rivalry between Michael and Robert Maxwell over Eleanor.

Eleanor's late brother, Nicky, with whom she lived for ten years. He introduced Eleanor to Robert Maxwell during her teens, when he was the Financial Correspondent of the *Daily Telegraph*.

Robert Maxwell with his new family

Robert Maxwell being naughty. He is looking at a woman's legs.
This is Eleanor's favourite photograph of him.

(Ian)   (Kevin)

Robert Maxwell's sons, Ian and Kevin. They appeared in court after
their father's death and were acquitted.

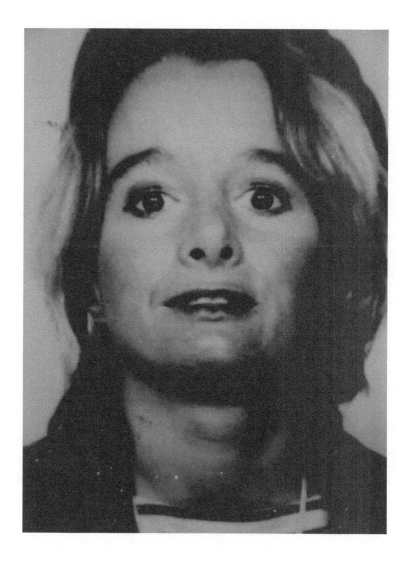

Eleanor listening to one of Robert Maxwell's Eve of Poll speeches

Robert Maxwell and his wife, Betty.

Robert Maxwell aged forty-seven, at the time of the 1970
Election campaign.

Robert Maxwell being ridiculed by *Private Eye* just after his funeral.
Eleanor went to the offices of *Private Eye* and sorted Ian Hislop out. She
was accompanied by her doctor, the late Dr Victor Ratner

Robert Maxwell and his wife, Betty with their baby girls. They are twins
and their names are Isabel and Christine.

Robert Maxwell with Eleanor

Robert Maxwell's favourite photograph of his wife Betty
when she was very young.